THE ULTIMATE
LOS ANGELES ANGELS
TRIVIA BOOK

A Collection of Amazing Trivia Quizzes
and Fun Facts for Die-Hard Angels Fans!

Ray Walker

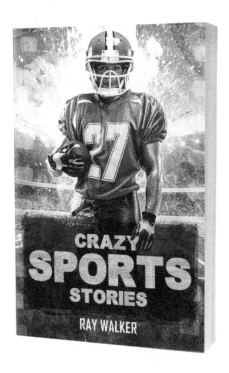

CONTENTS

INTRODUCTION

The Los Angeles Angels were established in 1961. Over the years, they have used different versions of their name. Whether the Los Angeles Angels, California Angels, Anaheim Angels, or Los Angeles Angels of Anaheim, they have consistently proven themselves to be a team who fights hard and is a force to be reckoned with in the MLB.

They currently hold one World Series championship, which they won in 2002. They have won one American League pennant, nine American League West division titles, and one Wild Card berth. They are very often a threat in the American League West Division, having last won it in 2014.

Baseball is a lot like life there are good times and bad times, good days, and bad days, but you have to do your absolute best to never give up. The Los Angeles Angels have proven that they refuse to give up and that they will do anything they need to do in order to bring a championship to the state of California.

Winning is more than possible when you have a storied past like the Angels do. They have so much captivating history and so many undeniable player legacies to be profoundly proud of. Especially considering the player's numbers that are already retired: Jim Fregosi, Gene Autry, Rod Carew, Nolan Ryan, Jimmie Reese, and, of course, Jackie Robinson.

The Los Angeles Angels currently call Angel Stadium home, which opened in 1966. They play in one of the most difficult divisions in baseball, the American League West, alongside the Oakland Athletics, Seattle Mariners, Texas Rangers, and Houston Astros.

With such a storied team past that goes back generations, you're probably already very knowledgeable as the die-hard Halos fan that you are. Let's test that knowledge to see if you truly are the world's biggest Angels fan.

All stats and information are current up to the 2020 season.

CHAPTER 1:

ORIGINS & HISTORY

QUIZ TIME!

1. Which of the following team names did the Angels franchise once go by?

    a. Anaheim Angels
    b. California Angels
    c. Golden State Angels
    d. Both A and B

2. In what year was the Los Angeles Angels franchise established?

    a. 1955
    b. 1959
    c. 1961
    d. 1968

3. The Angels' current home is Angel Stadium.

    a. True
    b. False

4. Which division do the Los Angeles Angels currently play in?

    a. American League Central
    b. American League West
    c. National League West
    d. National League Central

5. The Los Angeles Angels have never won a Wild Card berth.

    a. True
    b. False

6. How many American League pennants has the Los Angeles Angels franchise won?

    a. 0
    b. 1
    c. 2
    d. 3

7. What is the name of the Los Angeles Angels' unofficial mascot?

    a. Rally Mouse
    b. Rally Panda
    c. Rally Elephant
    d. Rally Monkey

8. Who is the winningest manager in Los Angeles Angels history?

    a. Dick Williams
    b. Bill Rigney

    c. Mike Scioscia

    d. Jim Fregosi

9. What is the name of the Los Angeles Angels' Triple A-Team, and where are they located?

    a. Salt Lake Bees

    b. Reno Aces

    c. Sacramento River Cats

    d. Las Vegas Aviators

10. Who was the first manager of the Angels franchise?

    a. Bobby Winkles

    b. Whitey Herzog

    c. Lefty Phillips

    d. Bill Rigney

11. The Los Angeles Angels were members of the National League West Division from 1969 to 1980.

    a. True

    b. False

12. What is the name of the Angels' current spring training home stadium?

    a. Hohokam Stadium

    b. Salt River Fields at Talking Stick

    c. Peoria Sports Complex

    d. Tempe Diablo Stadium

13. How many appearances has the Los Angeles Angels franchise made in the MLB playoffs?

a. 9

b. 10

c. 12

d. 15

14. How many World Series titles have the Los Angeles Angels won?

    a. 1

    b. 2

    c. 3

    d. 4

15. The Los Angeles Angels' current manager is Joe Maddon.

    a. True

    b. False

16. Which stadium was the first home of the Los Angeles Angels franchise?

    a. Angel Stadium

    b. Chavez Ravine

    c. Wrigley Field

    d. Dodger Stadium

17. Who is the current general manager of the Los Angeles Angels?

    a. Mike Rizzo

    b. Perry Minasian

    c. David Forst

    d. David Stearns

18. How many American League West division titles have the Los Angeles Angels won?

    a. 9

    b. 10

    c. 11

    d. 12

19. The Los Angeles Angels have been based in Anaheim, California, since 1966.

    a. True

    b. False

20. Arte Moreno became the first Mexican-American to own a major sports team in the United States when he purchased the Anaheim Angels from the Walt Disney Company back in 2003.

    a. True

    b. False

QUIZ ANSWERS

1. D – Both A and B

2. C – 1961

3. A – True

4. B – American League West

5. B – False (They won a berth in 2002.)

6. B – 1 (2002)

7. D – Rally Monkey

8. C – Mike Scioscia

9. D – Las Vegas Aviators

10. D – Bill Rigney

11. B – False

12. D – Tempe Diablo Stadium

13. B – 10

14. A – 1

15. A – True

16. C – Wrigley Field (in L.A.)

17. B – Perry Minasian

18. A – 9

19. A – True

20. A – True

DID YOU KNOW?

1. The Los Angeles Angels franchise has had 22 managers so far in their history. They include: Bill Rigney, Lefty Phillips, Del Rice, Bobby Winkles, Whitey Herzog, Dick Williams, Norm Sherry, Dave Garcia, Jim Fregosi, Gene Mauch, John McNamara, Cookie Rojas, Moose Stubing, Doug Rader, Buck Rodgers, Marcel Lachemann, Terry Collins, Mike Scioscia, Brad Ausmus, and Joe Maddon.

2. The Los Angeles Angels' current manager is Joe Maddon. He has previously managed the Tampa Bay Rays and Chicago Cubs. He is a three-time Manager of the Year Award winner and two-time World Series champion. He has worked in the Angels organization for over 30 years, as a minor league manager, scout, minor league hitting instructor, coach, and manager.

3. Mike Scioscia is the Los Angeles Angels' all-time winningest manager with a record of 1,650-1,428 (.536). Scioscia played as a catcher for the Los Angeles Dodgers from 1980 to 1992 and was the Angels' manager from 2000 to 2018.

4. Team Founder Gene Autry was the first person to have his number retired by the Los Angeles Angels. Number 26 was retired in 1982 because he was the team's "26th man." Autry was an American singer, songwriter, actor, musician, and rodeo performer.

5. The Los Angeles Angels have hosted three MLB All-Star Games in franchise history. The first one took place in 1967 at Anaheim Stadium, the second in 1989 at Anaheim Stadium, and the third in 2010 at Angel Stadium.

6. The Los Angeles Angels have had 11 no-hitters thrown in franchise history. The first occurred in 1962, thrown by Bo Belinsky, and the latest occurred in 2019, thrown by Taylor Cole and Felix Peña.

7. There has been one perfect game thrown in Los Angeles Angels history. It occurred in 1984 and was thrown by Mike Witt.

8. The Angels' Double-A team is the Rocket City Trash Pandas. Yes, the Trash Pandas. Other Angels' minor league teams include the Inland Empire 66ers, Burlington Bees, Orem Owlz, AZL Angels, and DSL Angels.

9. The Angels' unofficial mascot, the Rally Monkey, debuted on June 6, 2000. When down in the game, two video board operators took a clip of a monkey jumping around from the 1994 Jim Carrey movie *Ace Ventura: Pet Detective* and superimposed the words "RALLY MONKEY!" on top of it. The Angels scored two runs and ultimately won the game.

10. Jim Fregosi, a shortstop who wore number 11 from 1961 to 1971, and then managed them from 1978 to 1981, is the latest Angel to have his number retired by the team, when his jersey was hung in 1998.

CHAPTER 2:

JERSEYS & NUMBERS

QUIZ TIME!

1. The Los Angeles Angels have used ten different logos and three different color combinations throughout franchise history.

    a. True
    b. False

2. What are the Los Angeles Angels' official team colors?

    a. Red, navy blue, white
    b. Red, white, blue
    c. Red, navy blue, silver
    d. Red, silver, white

3. A new patch was added on the Angels' uniforms before the 2012 season featuring a red circle with the words "Angels Baseball" and the team logo inside with "1961" in the middle, which was the year the Angels franchise was established.

    a. True
    b. False

4. Which of the following numbers is NOT retired by the Los Angeles Angels?

    a. 11
    b. 22
    c. 29
    d. 30

5. What uniform number does Albert Pujols currently wear as a member of the Angels?

    a. 1
    b. 3
    c. 5
    d. 7

6. What uniform number did Tim Salmon wear during his time with the Angels?

    a. 5
    b. 15
    c. 25
    d. 50

7. Rickey Henderson's uniform number is retired by the Los Angeles Angels.

    a. True
    b. False

8. Keynan Middleton and which other player are the only two Angels players to have ever worn the uniform number 99 in franchise history?

    a. Tony Phillips
    b. Kevin Jepsen

c. Trevor Bell

d. Mitch Williams

9. Who is the only Angels player to have ever worn the uniform number 88?

   a. Shawn Wooten

   b. Ben Weber

   c. Rene Gonzales

   d. Reggie Willits

10. Uniform numbers 34 and 45 have been out of circulation within the Angels organization since the deaths of Nick Adenhart and Tyler Skaggs.

    a. True

    b. False

11. What uniform number did Chuck Finley wear as a member of the California/Anaheim Angels?

    a. 31

    b. 59

    c. 61

    d. Both A and B

12. What uniform number did Torii Hunter wear as a member of the Los Angeles Angels?

    a. 14

    b. 24

    c. 48

    d. 84

13. Vladimir Guerrero's number 27 is retired by the Los Angeles Angels.

    a. True
    b. False

14. What uniform number did Mark Langston wear as a member of the California/Anaheim Angels?

    a. 2
    b. 12
    c. 21
    d. 22

15. What uniform number did Darin Erstad wear as a member of the California/Anaheim Angels?

    a. 10
    b. 17
    c. 27
    d. Both B and C

16. What uniform number did Brian Downing wear as a member of the California/Anaheim Angels?

    a. 5
    b. 9
    c. 11
    d. Both A and B

17. During his time with the California Angels, Mike Witt wore the uniform number 44 and which other number?

    a. 19
    b. 29

c. 39

d. 49

18. What uniform number does Shohei Ohtani currently wear as a member of the Los Angeles Angels?

    a. 7

    b. 17

    c. 37

    d. 47

19. What uniform number did Frank Tanana wear as a member of the California Angels?

    a. 10

    b. 20

    c. 30

    d. 40

20. The Los Angeles Angels currently have six retired uniform numbers.

    a. True

    b. False

QUIZ ANSWERS

1. A – True

2. C – Red, navy blue, silver

3. A – True

4. B – 22

5. C – 5

6. B – 15

7. B – False

8. D – Mitch Williams

9. C – Rene Gonzales

10. A – True

11. D – Both A and B

12. C – 48

13. B – False (Mike Trout currently wears number 27.)

14. B – 12

15. D – Both B and C

16. D – Both A and B

17. C – 39

18. B – 17

19. D – 40

20. A – True

DID YOU KNOW?

1. The Angels have retired six uniform numbers so far: Jim Fregosi (number 11), Gene Autry (number 26), Rod Carew (number 29), Nolan Ryan (number 30), Jackie Robinson (number 42), and Jimmie Reese (number 50).

2. Yunel Escobar is the only player in Angels franchise history so far to wear the uniform number 0.

3. Brennan Boesch is the only player is Angels franchise history so far to wear the uniform number 00.

4. Trevor Bell is the only player is Angels franchise history so far to wear the uniform number 70.

5. During his time with the Los Angeles Angels, John Lackey wore the uniform number 41.

6. During his time with the Anaheim/Los Angeles Angels, Chone Figgins wore the uniform numbers 6 and 9.

7. Jackie Robinson's number 42 is retired by the Angels as well as the MLB as a whole. No Angels or MLB player will ever wear number 42 again. The Yankees' Mariano Rivera was the last player to wear it.

8. During his time with the California/Anaheim Angels, Jim Edmonds wore the uniform number 25.

9. During his time with the California/Anaheim Angels, Troy Glaus wore the uniform numbers 12, 14, and 25.

10. During his time with the California Angels, Bobby Grich wore the uniform number 4.

CHAPTER 3:

SLAMMIN' SALMON

QUIZ TIME!

1. What is Tim Salmon's full name?

    a. Nathaniel Timothy Salmon

    b. Timothy Nathaniel Salmon

    c. Timothy James Salmon

    d. James Timothy Salmon

2. Tim Salmon made his debut with the California Angels in 1992.

    a. True

    b. False

3. Where was Tim Salmon born?

    a. San Diego, California

    b. Long Beach, California

    c. Phoenix, Arizona

    d. Tuscon, Arizona

4. When was Tim Salmon born?

    a. August 24, 1968
    b. August 24, 1978
    c. April 24, 1968
    d. April 24, 1978

5. Tim Salmon was named the American League Rookie of the Year in 1993?

    a. True
    b. False

6. How many MLB All-Stars Games was Tim Salmon named to in his career?

    a. 0
    b. 1
    c. 2
    d. 3

7. How many home runs did Tim Salmon hit during his 14-season MLB career?

    a. 259
    b. 279
    c. 299
    d. 309

8. Tim Salmon played his entire 14-season MLB career with the Los Angeles Angels.

    a. True
    b. False

9. What year did Tim Salmon win his sole Silver Slugger Award?

    a. 1992
    b. 1993
    c. 1994
    d. 1995

10. How many RBI did Tim Salmon collect during his 14-season MLB career?

    a. 1,006
    b. 1,016
    c. 1,056
    d. 1,096

11. How many at-bats did Tim Salmon have during his MLB career?

    a. 5,034
    b. 5,234
    c. 5,534
    d. 5,934

12. Tim Salmon did NOT win a World Series championship during his MLB career.

    a. True
    b. False

13. How many stolen bases did Tim Salmon collect during his 14-season MLB career?

    a. 28
    b. 38

c. 48

d. 78

14. Tim Salmon missed the entire 2005 MLB season due to injury.

  a. True

  b. False

15. How many times was Tim Salmon named the American League Player of the Week during his 14-season MLB career?

  a. 1

  b. 2

  c. 5

  d. 8

16. How many times was Tim Salmon named the American League Player of the Month during his 14-season MLB career?

  a. 1

  b. 2

  c. 3

  d. 4

17. Tim Salmon is member of the National Baseball Hall of Fame.

  a. True

  b. False

18. Where did Tim Salmon attend college?

    a. Arizona State University
    b. Grand Canyon University
    c. Long Beach State University
    d. He did not attend college

19. What is Tim Salmon's career batting average?

    a. .252
    b. .262
    c. .272
    d. .282

20. Tim Salmon was awarded the 2002 Hutch Award, which honors the legacy of former MLB Player Fred Hutchinson.

    a. True
    b. False

QUIZ ANSWERS

1. C – Timothy James Salmon

2. A – True

3. B – Long Beach, California

4. A – August 24, 1968

5. A – True

6. A – 0

7. C – 299

8. A – True

9. D – 1995

10. B – 1,016

11. D – 5,934

12. B – False (He won a World Series in 2002.)

13. C – 48

14. A – True

15. C – 5

16. A – 1

17. B – False

18. B – Grand Canyon University

19. D - .282

20. A – True

DID YOU KNOW?

1. Tim Salmon was inducted into the Los Angeles Angels Hall of Fame in 2015.

2. Since 2014, Tim Salmon has been an analyst on Angels pre- and postgame shows on Fox Sports West.

3. "My ability to throw a baseball was a gift. It was a God-given gift and I am truly appreciative of that gift." – Nolan Ryan

4. Tim Salmon has the highest home run total of all players who have never been selected for an MLB All-Star Game.

5. With 986, as of 2021, Tim Salmon ranks second all-time in Angels history in runs scored.

6. Tim Salmon played his final MLB game on October 1, 2006, against the Oakland A's.

7. Tim Salmon played for the California, Anaheim, and Los Angeles Angels.

8. Tim Salmon won the MVP Award in the 2010 MLB All-Star Legends and Celebrity Softball Game, held at Angel Stadium.

9. Tim Salmon's career WAR is 40.6.

10. Tim Salmon collected 1,674 hits over the course of his 14-season MLB career.

CHAPTER 4:

CATCHY NICKNAMES

QUIZ TIME!

1. What nickname did Hideki Matsui go by?

    a. Big Mat

    b. Godzilla

    c. Hittin Hideki

    d. Frankenstein

2. Current Angels manager Joe Maddon gave his RV a nickname. That nickname is "Cousin Eddie."

    a. True

    b. False

3. What is a nickname that the Angels as a team are referred to as?

    a. The Boys in Silver

    b. The Boys in Red

    c. The Halos

    d. The A's

4. What nickname did Reggie Jackson go by?

    a. Mr. Home Run

    b. Mr. October

    c. Mr. September

    d. Runnin' Reggie

5. What nickname did Dave Winfield go by?

    a. Mr. Speed

    b. Divin' Dave

    c. Win

    d. Daddy Longlegs

6. Which nickname does Shane Victorino go by?

    a. Vic

    b. Super Shane

    c. The Flyin' Hawaiian

    d. Aloha

7. Nap Lajoie went by the nicknames, "Nap," "Larry," and "The Frenchman." His given first name was Napoleon.

    a. True

    b. False

8. What is J.T. Snow's full name?

    a. James Thomas Snow Jr.

    b. Jonathan Thomas Snow Jr.

    c. Jacob Thomas Snow Jr.

    d. Jack Thomas Snow Jr.

9. "Albert" is a nickname. What is Albert Pujols's full name?

  a. Ricardo Alberto Pujols Alcántara
  b. Ricardo Alberto Pujols
  c. José Alberto Pujols
  d. José Alberto Pujols Alcántara

10. "Whitey" is a nickname. What is former Angels manager Herzog's full name?

  a. Lorrel Elvert Norman Herzog
  b. Lorrel Norman Elvert Herzog
  c. Dorrel Norman Elvert Herzog
  d. Dorrel Elvert Norman Herzog

11. What nickname does Jason Grilli go by?

  a. G-Man
  b. Griller
  c. Grill Cheese
  d. J Grill

12. Doug Rader went by the nicknames "Rojo" and "The Red Rooster."

  a. True
  b. False

13. What is former Angels pitcher C.J. Wilson's full name?

  a. Cody James Wilson
  b. Christopher James Wilson
  c. Christopher John Wilson
  d. Cody John Wilson

14. What is former Angel Mark Teixeira's nickname?

    a. Tex

    b. Marky T

    c. Tex Mex

    d. M.T.

15. Tris Speaker went by the nicknames "Tris" and "The Gray Eagle." His real first name was Tristram.

    a. True

    b. False

16. What nickname does Bartolo Colon go by?

    a. Mr. Hungry

    b. Little Sexy

    c. Tolo-Colo

    d. Big Sexy

17. Tim Lincecum's nickname is "The Freak."

    a. True

    b. False

18. What nickname does Tim Salmon NOT go by?

    a. Mr. Angel

    b. Kingfish

    c. Slammin' Salmon

    d. Mr. Fishy

19. What nickname did Don Sutton go by?

    a. Black & Decker

    b. The Mechanic

c. Mr. Los Angeles

d. Both A and B

20. Andrelton Simmons goes by the nickname "Simba."

a. True

b. False

QUIZ ANSWERS

1. B – Godzilla

2. A – True

3. C – The Halos

4. B – Mr. October

5. D – Daddy Longlegs

6. C – The Flyin' Hawaiian

7. A – True

8. D – Jack Thomas Snow Jr.

9. D – José Alberto Pujols Alcántara

10. C – Dorrel Norman Elvert Herzog

11. C – Grill Cheese

12. A – True

13. C – Christopher John Wilson

14. A – Tex

15. A – True

16. D – Big Sexy

17. A – True

18. D – Mr. Fishy

19. D – Both A and B

20. A – True

DID YOU KNOW?

1. Former Angel Mitch Williams went by the nickname "Wild Thing," but it had nothing to do with the movie *Major League*. The nickname came about because of his wild pitching delivery.

2. Angels manager Joe Maddon goes by the nickname "Broad Street Joe."

3. Rickey Henderson is often referred to as "The Man of Steal."

4. Jim Fregosi went by the nickname "Skip."

5. Former Angel Jim Edmonds was often referred to as "Jimmy Baseball."

6. Erick Aybar goes by the nickname "Admiral."

7. David Eckstein went by the nicknames "X Factor" and "Just Enough."

8. Bengie Molina went by the nickname "Big Money."

9. Mike Napoli goes by the nickname "Porterhouse."

10. Bert Campaneris is often referred to as "Campy."

CHAPTER 5:

TROUT

QUIZ TIME!

1. What is Mike Trout's full name?

    a. Joseph Michael Trout

    b. Michael Joseph Trout

    c. Nelson Michael Trout

    d. Michael Nelson Trout

2. Mike Trout made his debut with the Los Angeles Angels in 2011.

    a. True

    b. False

3. Where was Mike Trout born?

    a. San Diego, California

    b. Fullerton, California

    c. Vineland, New Jersey

    d. Trenton, New Jersey

4. When was Mike Trout born?

    a. August 7, 1989

    b. August 7, 1991

    c. April 7, 1989

    d. April 7, 1991

5. Mike Trout was named the American League Rookie of the Year in 2012.

    a. True

    b. False

6. How many MLB All-Star Games has Mike Trout been named to in his career.

    a. 5

    b. 6

    c. 7

    d. 8

7. Mike Trout was drafted in the 1st round of the 2009 MLB Draft in which position overall?

    a. 2nd

    b. 11th

    c. 25th

    d. 29th

8. Mike Trout attended Cal State Fullerton.

    a. True

    b. False

9. Mike Trout won the Wilson Defensive Player of the Year Award in which year?

    a. 2012

    b. 2013

    c. 2014

    d. All of the above

10. How many home runs did Mike Trout hit during the 2019 season?

    a. 38

    b. 41

    c. 45

    d. 50

11. How many times has Mike Trout been named the American League MVP in his career?

    a. 1

    b. 2

    c. 3

    d. 4

12. Mike Trout led the American League in RBIs in 2014.

    a. True

    b. False

13. Mike Trout led the American League in stolen bases in which year?

    a. 2012

    b. 2015

    c. 2016

    d. 2018

14. Mike Trout hit for the cycle on May 21, 2013.

    a. True

    b. False

15. How many times has Mike Trout won a Silver Slugger Award in his career?

    a. 4

    b. 6

    c. 7

    d. 8

16. Mike Trout won the American League Hank Aaron Award in which year?

    a. 2012

    b. 2014

    c. 2019

    d. Both B and C

17. Mike Trout became a member of the 30-30 club in 2012.

    a. True

    b. False

18. How many bases did Mike Trout steal during the 2012 season?

    a. 39

    b. 45

    c. 49

    d. 55

19. What uniform number does Mike Trout wear?

    a. 1

    b. 2

    c. 27

    d. 45

20. Mike Trout scored 129 runs during the 2012 season.

    a. True

    b. False

QUIZ ANSWERS

1. D – Michael Nelson Trout

2. A – True

3. C – Vineland, New Jersey

4. B – August 7, 1991

5. A – True

6. D – 8

7. C – 25th

8. B – False (He did not go to college.)

9. A – 2012

10. C – 45

11. C – 3 (2014, 2016, 2019)

12. A – True

13. A – 2012

14. A – True

15. D – 8 (2012-2016, 2018-2020)

16. D – Both B and C

17. A – True

18. C – 49

19. C – 27

20. A – True

DID YOU KNOW?

1. In February 2014, President Barack Obama used Trout as an analogy for the 2014 U.S. Farm Bill. To emphasize the versatility of the bill, Obama remarked that it was "like Mike Trout, for those of you who know baseball... somebody who's got a lot of tools."

2. Trout and his wife Jessica have a son named Beckham, who was born in 2020.

3. Trout is a fan of the Philadelphia Flyers, Philadelphia 76ers, and Philadelphia Eagles. He even holds season tickets for the Eagles.

4. On August 23, 2020, a Mike Trout trading card sold for $3.93 million at auction, breaking the record for the most expensive sale price for a sports card.

5. Mike Trout has his own line of shoes with Nike.

6. Mike Trout is a partner and investor in Bodyarmor SuperDrink and has a sponsorship deal with SuperPretzel. He is also endorsed by Nike, Rawlings, Topps, and J&J Snack Foods.

7. Mike Trout led the American League in wins above replacement (WAR) in each of his first five full seasons.

8. In 2019, Mike Trout signed a 12-year, $426 million contract with the Angels, the second richest contract in the history

of North American sports and professional sports in general, and the biggest contract at the time of signing.

9. Mike Trout grew up a Philadelphia Phillies fan, and attended their World Series parade in 2008.

10. Mike Trout's father Jeff was drafted by the Minnesota Twins in 1983.

CHAPTER 6:

STATISTICALLY SPEAKING

QUIZ TIME!

1. Mike Trout currently holds the Los Angeles Angels franchise record for the most home runs. How many has he hit as of the end of the 2020 season?

   a. 299

   b. 302

   c. 312

   d. 322

2. Pitcher Chuck Finley has the most wins in Los Angeles Angels franchise history, with 165.

   a. True

   b. False

3. Which pitcher holds the Los Angeles Angels record for most career shutouts thrown, with 40?

   a. Frank Tanana

   b. Dean Chance

c. Mike Witt

d. Nolan Ryan

4. Which two Los Angeles Angels batters are tied for the single-season record for strikeouts, with 184 each?

a. Josh Hamilton and Mike Trout

b. Kole Calhoun and Mark Trumbo

c. Mike Trout and Mark Trumbo

d. Kole Calhoun and Mike Trout

5. Which pitcher has the most strikeouts in Los Angeles Angels franchise history, with a whopping 2,416?

a. Chuck Finley

b. Nolan Ryan

c. Jered Weaver

d. Mike Witt

6. Who has the most stolen bases in Los Angeles Angels franchise history, with 280?

a. Mike Trout

b. Gary Pettis

c. Chone Figgins

d. Darin Erstad

7. Troy Percival holds the record for most saves in Los Angeles Angels history, with 316.

a. True

b. False

8. Who holds the Los Angeles Angels record for being intentionally walked, with 112?

a. Albert Pujols

b. Chili Davis

c. Mike Trout

d. Vladimir Guerrero

9. Which player holds the Los Angeles Angels franchise record for home runs in a single season, with 47?

a. Mike Trout

b. Troy Glaus

c. Albert Pujols

d. Vladimir Guerrero

10. Which batter holds the single-season, Los Angeles Angels record for hits, with 240?

a. Garret Anderson

b. Alex Johnson

c. Vladimir Guerrero

d. Darin Erstad

11. Who holds the single-season, Los Angeles Angels record for double plays grounded into, with 28?

a. Albert Pujols

b. Vladimir Guerrero

c. Howie Kendrick

d. Torii Hunter

12. Garret Anderson holds the record for the most sacrifice flies in Los Angeles Angels all-time franchise history, with 76.

a. True

b. False

13. Chuck Finley threw the greatest number of wild pitches in Los Angeles Angels franchise history, with how many missing their mark?

    a. 87

    b. 97

    c. 117

    d. 127

14. Chone Figgins holds the Los Angeles Angels single-season record for most triples. How many did he hit in his record 2004 season?

    a. 12

    b. 17

    c. 20

    d. 27

15. Which hitter has the most walks in Los Angeles Angels franchise history, with 970?

    a. Tim Salmon

    b. Brian Downing

    c. Bobby Grich

    d. Rod Carew

16. Which Los Angeles Angels hitter holds the all-time franchise record for best overall batting average at .319?

    a. Jim Edmonds

    b. Howie Kendrick

    c. Rod Carew

    d. Vladimir Guerrero

17. Tim Salmon holds the Los Angeles Angels record for most runs scored, with 1,024.

    a. True
    b. False

18. Who has the most plate appearances all time in Los Angeles Angels franchise history, with 8,480?

    a. Tim Salmon
    b. Jim Fregosi
    c. Garret Anderson
    d. Albert Pujols

19. Which pitcher holds the Los Angeles Angels franchise record for most saves in a single season, with 62?

    a. Bryan Harvey
    b. Tony Percival
    c. Brian Fuentes
    d. Francisco Rodriguez

20. Chuck Finley holds the Los Angeles Angels franchise record for most losses, with 140.

    a. True
    b. False

QUIZ ANSWERS

1. B – 302

2. A – True

3. D – Nolan Ryan

4. C – Mike Trout and Mark Trumbo

5. B – Nolan Ryan

6. C – Chone Figgins

7. A – True

8. D – Vladimir Guerrero

9. B – Troy Glaus (2000)

10. D – Darin Erstad (2000)

11. A – Albert Pujols (2014)

12. A – True

13. C – 117

14. B – 17

15. A – Tim Salmon

16. D – Vladimir Guerrero

17. B – False (Garret Anderson holds this record.)

18. C – Garret Anderson

19. D – Francisco Rodriguez (2008)

20. A – True

DID YOU KNOW?

1. Chuck Finley threw the most innings in Los Angeles Angels franchise history, with 2,675.0. Coming in second is Nolan Ryan who threw 2,181.1 innings.

2. Darin Erstad had the best single-season batting average in Los Angeles Angels franchise history at .355 in 2000. Coming in second is Rod Carew whose batting average was .339 in 1983.

3. Mike Trout holds the Los Angeles Angels franchise record for stolen base percentage, with 84.45% accuracy. Chone Figgins holds the Los Angeles Angels franchise record for stolen bases, with 280, and Figgins holds the franchise record for the most times caught stealing, with 96.

4. Garret Anderson has the most extra-base hits in Los Angeles Angels franchise history, with 796. Second on the list is Tim Salmon with 662.

5. Mike Trout holds the Los Angeles Angels franchise record for at-bats per home run at 15.0. Essentially, what this means is that, on average, Trout hits a home run about every 15 at-bats.

6. Troy Percival holds the Los Angeles Angels franchise record for strikeouts per nine innings pitched at 10.432. Essentially, what this means is that, during his time with the Angels, Percival recorded about 10-11 strikeouts in every nine innings that he pitched.

46

7. David Eckstein holds the single-season, Los Angeles Angels record for the most hit by pitches with 27 in 2002. Tom Murphy holds the single-season, Los Angeles Angels record for most batters hit with 21 in 1969.

8. Garret Anderson holds the Los Angeles Angels franchise record for career doubles hit, with 489. Second on the list is Tim Salmon with 339.

9. Nolan Ryan and Clyde Wright are tied for the Los Angeles Angels single-season record for wins, with 22 each.

10. Four pitchers are tied for the Los Angeles Angels single-season record for losses, with 19 each. They are George Brunet, Kirk McCaskill, Frank Tanana, and Clyde Wright.

CHAPTER 7:

THE TRADE MARKET

QUIZ TIME!

1. On December 10, 1971 the California Angels traded which player to the New York Mets for Nolan Ryan, Don Rose, LeRoy Stanton, and Francisco Estrada?

    a. Sandy Alomar

    b. Jim Spencer

    c. Jim Fregosi

    d. Ken McMullen

2. On February 3, 1979 the California Angels traded Ken Landreaux, Dave Engle, Paul Hartzell, and Brad Havens to the Minnesota Twins for which player?

    a. Don Baylor

    b. Rod Carew

    c. Joe Rudi

    d. Carney Lansford

3. The Los Angeles Angels have NEVER made a trade with the Los Angeles Dodgers.

a. True

b. False

4. On December 5, 1977 the California Angels traded Bobby Bonds, Thad Bosley, and Richard Dotson to which team for Brian Downing, Chris Knapp, and Dave Frost?

   a. St. Louis Cardinals

   b. New York Yankees

   c. San Francisco Giants

   d. Chicago White Sox

5. The Los Angeles Angels have only made seven trades with the Arizona Diamondbacks all time.

   a. True

   b. False

6. On November 28, 1972 the California Angels traded Andy Messersmith and Ken McMullen to which team for Frank Robinson, Bill Singer, Mike Strahler, Bill Grabarkewitz, and Bobby Valentine?

   a. Cincinnati Reds

   b. Baltimore Orioles

   c. Los Angeles Dodgers

   d. Cleveland Indians

7. On July 29, 2008 the Los Angeles Angels traded Casey Kotchman and Steve Marek to the Atlanta Braves for which player?

   a. Maicer Izturis

   b. Mark Teixeira

c. Kendrys Morales

d. Erick Aybar

8. On July 25, 2010 the Los Angeles Angels traded Patrick Corbin, Tyler Skaggs, Joe Saunders, and Rafael Rodriguez to which team for Dan Haren?

    a. Los Angeles Dodgers

    b. Washington Nationals

    c. St. Louis Cardinals

    d. Arizona Diamondbacks

9. On July 27, 2012 the Los Angeles Angels traded Jean Segura, Johnny Hellweg, and Ariel Peña to the Milwaukee Brewers for which player?

    a. Alberto Callaspo

    b. Zack Greinke

    c. Ervin Santana

    d. C.J. Wilson

10. The Los Angeles Angels have made only five trades with the Colorado Rockies all time.

    a. True

    b. False

11. On March 23, 2000 the Anaheim Angels traded Jim Edmonds to which team for Adam Kennedy and Kent Bottenfield?

    a. San Diego Padres

    b. Chicago Cubs

    c. St. Louis Cardinals

    d. Milwaukee Brewers

12. The Los Angeles Angels have made only five trades with the Miami/Florida Marlins all time (as of the end of the 2020 season).

   a. True
   b. False

13. How many trades have the Los Angeles Angels made with the Tampa Bay Rays all time?

   a. 7
   b. 11
   c. 14
   d. 21

14. On November 12, 2015 the Atlanta Braves traded Jose Briceno and Andrelton Simmons to the Los Angeles Angels for Erick Aybar, Chris Ellis, Sean Newcomb, and cash considerations.

   a. True
   b. False

15. On July 13, 2001 the Anaheim Angels traded Kimera Bartee to the Colorado Rockies for which player?

   a. Wally Joyner
   b. David Eckstein
   c. Troy Glaus
   d. Chone Figgins

16. On October 21, 2011 the Los Angeles Angels traded Mike Napoli and Juan Rivera to which team for Vernon Wells?

   a. Boston Red Sox
   b. New York Yankees

c. Toronto Blue Jays

d. Texas Rangers

17. On October 28, 1996 the California Angels traded which player to the Kansas City Royals for Mark Gubicza and Mike Bovee?

a. J.T. Snow

b. Chili Davis

c. Mark Langston

d. Chuck Finley

18. On May 11, 1982 the California Angels traded Tom Brunansky and Mike Walters to which team for Doug Corbett and Rob Wilfong?

a. Baltimore Orioles

b. St. Louis Cardinals

c. Boston Red Sox

d. Minnesota Twins

19. On April 4, 1977 the California Angels traded Mike Easler to which team for Randy Sealy?

a. Houston Astros

b. Boston Red Sox

c. Pittsburgh Pirates

d. Philadelphia Phillies

20. At the trade deadline in 1996, the California Angels traded Damian Easley for Greg Gohr.

a. True

b. False

QUIZ ANSWERS

1. C – Jim Fregosi

2. B – Rod Carew

3. B – False (There have been 15 trades as of the end of the 2020 season.)

4. D – Chicago White Sox

5. A – True

6. C – Los Angeles Dodgers

7. B – Mark Teixeira

8. D – Arizona Diamondbacks

9. B – Zack Greinke

10. A – True

11. C – St. Louis Cardinals

12. A – True

13. B – 11

14. A – True

15. D – Chone Figgins

16. C – Toronto Blue Jays

17. B – Chili Davis

18. D – Minnesota Twins

19. C – Pittsburgh Pirates

20. A – True

DID YOU KNOW?

1. On December 2, 1990 the California Angels traded Devon White and Willie Fraser to the Toronto Blue Jays for Luis Soto and Junior Felix.

2. On November 27, 1996 the California Angels traded J.T. Snow to the San Francisco Giants for Allen Watson and Fausto Macey.

3. On December 10, 1980 the California Angels traded Carney Lansford, Mark Clear, and Rick Miller to the Boston Red Sox for Rick Burleson and Butch Hobson.

4. On November 19, 2007 the Los Angeles Angels of Anaheim traded Orlando Cabrera to the Chicago White Sox for Jon Garland.

5. On March 14, 1991 the California Angels traded Dante Bichette to the Milwaukee Brewers for Dave Parker.

6. On December 19, 2012 the Los Angeles Angels traded Kendrys Morales to the Seattle Mariners for Jason Vargas.

7. On July 29, 2013 the Los Angeles Angels traded Scott Downs to the Atlanta Braves for Cory Rasmus.

8. On October 31, 2012 the Kansas City Royals traded Brandon Sisk to the Los Angeles Angels for Ervin Santana and cash considerations.

9. On November 5, 2014 the Los Angeles Angels traded Hank Conger to the Houston Astros for Nick Tropeano and Carlos Perez.

10. As of the end of the 2020 season the Los Angeles Angels have made 24 trades with the Oakland A's.

CHAPTER 8:

DRAFT DAY

QUIZ TIME!

1. With which overall pick in the 1st round of the 2004 MLB Draft, the Anaheim Angels selected Jered Weaver?

    a. 1st

    b. 2nd

    c. 12th

    d. 27th

2. Which team selected Bobby Grich with the 19th overall pick in the 1st round of the 1967 MLB Draft?

    a. St. Louis Cardinals

    b. Boston Red Sox

    c. New York Yankees

    d. Baltimore Orioles

3. In the 10th round of which MLB Draft, the Anaheim Angels selected Howie Kendrick?

    a. 2000

    b. 2002

c. 2003

d. 2004

4. In which round of the 1990 MLB Draft, the California Angels selected Garret Anderson?

    a. 1st

    b. 2nd

    c. 3rd

    d. 4th

5. In the 2nd round of which MLB Draft, the Anaheim Angels selected John Lackey?

    a. 1999

    b. 2000

    c. 2001

    d. 2002

6. In the 4th round of the 1997 MLB Draft, the _____ selected Chone Figgins.

    a. Los Angeles Dodgers

    b. Seattle Mariners

    c. Colorado Rockies

    d. New York Mets

7. Mike Witt was drafted by the California Angels in the 4th round of the 1978 MLB Draft.

    a. True

    b. False

8. Which team selected Andrelton Simmons in the 2nd round of the 2010 MLB Draft?

a. San Diego Padres

b. Atlanta Braves

c. Milwaukee Brewers

d. Cincinnati Reds

9. With the 20th overall pick in the 1st round of the 1993 MLB Draft, which team selected Torii Hunter?

a. Detroit Tigers

b. Oakland A's

c. Los Angeles Dodgers

d. Minnesota Twins

10. The California Angels drafted Jarrod Washburn in the 2nd round of the 1995 MLB Draft.

a. True

b. False

11. Jim Edmonds was drafted in which round of the 1988 MLB Draft by the California Angels?

a. 2nd

b. 4th

c. 7th

d. 12th

12. Frank Tanana was drafted by the California Angels in the 1st round (13th overall) of the 1971 MLB Draft.

a. True

b. False

13. In which round of the 1999 MLB Draft, the St. Louis Cardinals selected Albert Pujols?

a. 1st

b. 3rd

c. 8th

d. 13th

14. Anthony Rendon was drafted in the 1st round (6th overall) of the 2011 MLB Draft by which team?

    a. Atlanta Braves

    b. Washington Nationals

    c. New York Mets

    d. Los Angeles Dodgers

15. Kole Calhoun was drafted in which round of the 2010 MLB Draft by the Los Angeles Angels.

    a. 4th

    b. 6th

    c. 8th

    d. 15th

16. C.J. Wilson was drafted in the 5th round of the 2001 MLB Draft by the which team?

    a. Chicago Cubs

    b. Texas Rangers

    c. Seattle Mariners

    d. Arizona Diamondbacks

17. David Eckstein was drafted in the 19th round of the 1997 MLB Draft by the which team?

    a. Boston Red Sox

    b. St. Louis Cardinals

c. Arizona Diamondbacks

d. San Diego Padres

18. Adam Kennedy was drafted in the 1st round, 20th overall, of the 1997 MLB Draft by which team?

a. Oakland A's

b. Seattle Mariners

c. Los Angeles Dodgers

d. St. Louis Cardinals

19. Carney Lansford was drafted in which round of the 1975 MLB Draft by the California Angels.

a. 1st

b. 2nd

c. 3rd

d. 6th

20. Don Baylor was drafted by the Baltimore Orioles in the 2nd round of the 1967 MLB Draft.

a. True

b. False

QUIZ ANSWERS

1. C – 12th

2. D – Baltimore Orioles

3. B – 2002

4. D – 4th

5. A – 1999

6. C – Colorado Rockies

7. A – True

8. B – Atlanta Braves

9. D – Minnesota Twins

10. A – True

11. C – 7th

12. A – True

13. D – 13th

14. B – Washington Nationals

15. C – 8th

16. B – Texas Rangers

17. A – Boston Red Sox

18. D – St. Louis Cardinals

19. C – 3rd

20. A – True

DID YOU KNOW?

1. Chili Davis was drafted in the 11th round of the 1997 MLB Draft by the San Francisco Giants.

2. Huston Street was drafted in the 1st round (40th overall) of the 2004 MLB Draft by the Oakland A's.

3. Mike Napoli was drafted in the 17th round of the 2000 MLB Draft by the Anaheim Angels.

4. Wally Joyner was drafted in the 3rd round of the 1983 MLB Draft by the California Angels.

5. Dave Winfield was drafted in the 1st round (4th overall) of the 1973 MLB Draft by the San Diego Padres.

6. Mark Trumbo was drafted in the 18th round of the 2004 MLB Draft by the Anaheim Angels.

7. Dan Haren was drafted in the 2nd round of the 2001 MLB Draft by the St. Louis Cardinals.

8. Darin Erstad was drafted in the 1st round (1st overall) of the 1995 MLB Draft by the California Angels.

9. Tim Salmon was drafted in the 3rd round of the 1989 MLB Draft by the California Angels.

10. Rickey Henderson was drafted in the 4th round of the 1976 MLB Draft by the Oakland A's.

CHAPTER 9:

ODDS & ENDS

QUIZ TIME!

1. Which reality TV show did former Angel Jim Edmonds star on with his ex-wife Meghan?

   a. *90 Day Fiancé*

   b. *Survivor*

   c. *The Real Housewives of Orange County*

   d. *Celebrity Big Brother*

2. Jered Weaver named his son after fallen teammate Nick Adenhart.

   a. True

   b. False

3. Former Angels manager Mike Scioscia has appeared in two episodes of which animated TV show?

   a. *Family Guy*

   b. *Bob's Burgers*

   c. *SpongeBob SquarePants*

   d. *The Simpsons*

4. What does Josh Hamilton have tattooed on his left arm?

    a. A portrait of Alexander Hamilton
    b. "Hambone"
    c. A pig
    d. "Hammy"

5. Former Angels pitcher C.J. Wilson holds a charitable event each year featuring which popular video game?

    a. *Mario Party*
    b. *Fortnite*
    c. *Call of Duty*
    d. *Guitar Hero*

6. During the 1990s and early 2000s, Nolan Ryan was a spokesman for which popular pain reliever brand?

    a. Excedrin
    b. Aleve
    c. Advil
    d. Tylenol

7. Current Angels manager Joe Maddon has a serious passion for cycling. He says he bikes anywhere from 60 to 100 miles per week. He loves staying in shape, plus the mental benefits cycling provides him.

    a. True
    b. False

8. While in college, what was former Angels' outfielder Dave Winfield arrested for stealing?

    a. Snowblower
    b. Bag of chips

c. Baseball glove

d. Lawn mower

9. Shane Victorino was on an episode of which popular television show, playing a character named Shaun?

   a. *CSI*

   b. *Law & Order SVU*

   c. *Hawaii Five-0*

   d. *NCIS*

10. Zack Greinke is a minority owner of a which food franchise?

    a. In-N-Out

    b. Dunkin' Donuts

    c. Chipotle

    d. Ben & Jerry's

11. Mark Langston appeared in a 1997 episode of which popular television show, entitled "To Tell a Mortal"?

    a. *The Fresh Prince of Bel Air*

    b. *Home Improvement*

    c. *Full House*

    d. *Sabrina, the Teenage Witch*

12. Albert Pujols scored 100% on his U.S. Citizenship test.

    a. True

    b. False

13. In 2003, former Angel Frank Robinson guest starred in an episode of which popular television series alongside MLB legends Ernie Banks and Johnny Bench?

a. *King of Queens*

b. *Seinfeld*

c. *Everybody Loves Raymond*

d. *Yes, Dear*

14. Andrelton Simmons was born in the Netherlands.

    a. True

    b. False

15. In a 1994 episode of which popular television series, Dave Winfield appeared alongside other MLB players as themselves during the MLB strike?

    a. *Friends*

    b. *The Fresh Prince of Bel Air*

    c. *Married… with Children*

    d. *Sister, Sister*

16. Rickey Henderson is known for referring to himself in the third person.

    a. True

    b. False

17. What does Howie Kendrick have a vintage collection of?

    a. Mugs

    b. Watches

    c. Dolls

    d. Cameras

18. What year was Disney's *Angels in the Outfield* released?

    a. 1992

    b. 1993

c. 1994

d. 1995

19. Former Angel Bert Campaneris is the cousin of which other former Angel?

    a. Tom Satriano

    b. Jose Cardenal

    c. Marcelino Lopez

    d. Minnie Rojas

20. On December 9, 2019, Mike Napoli was hired by the Chicago Cubs as their quality assurance coach.

    a. True

    b. False

QUIZ ANSWERS

1. C – *The Real Housewives of Orange County*

2. A – True

3. D – *The Simpsons*

4. B – "Hambone"

5. D – *Guitar Hero*

6. C – Advil

7. A – True

8. A – Snowblower

9. C – *Hawaii Five-0*

10. C – Chipotle

11. D – *Sabrina, the Teenage Witch*

12. A – True

13. D – *Yes, Dear*

14. A – True

15. C – *Married… with Children*

16. A – True

17. B – Watches

18. C – 1994

19. B – Jose Cardenal

20. A – True

DID YOU KNOW?

1. In his first college game, Albert Pujols hit a grand slam and turned an unassisted triple play.

2. Bengie Molina is now a color analyst for St. Louis Cardinals Spanish radio broadcasts.

3. Former Angels manager, Cookie Rojas's son, Victor is now a play-by-play announcer for the Los Angeles Angels.

4. Vernon Wells's father is an acclaimed sports artist and was an early contributor to Upper Deck baseball cards. For over 30 years, Vernon Wells Sr. has been creating works of art for players, card companies, posters, media guide covers, and more. According to his website, he has focused specifically on marketing to players in sports.

5. Max Stassi's great uncle, Myril Hoag, played in three World Series. He played from 1931 to 1945 for the New York Yankees, St. Louis Browns, Chicago White Sox, and Cleveland Indians. Max's brother Brock also played in the MLB.

6. During Darin Erstad's time with the Angels, his hometown carried all Angels games over the radio; even though most North Dakota stations only carry Minnesota Twins games. Erstad was born in Jamestown, North Dakota, in 1976.

7. When Bartolo Colon was 42 years old, he became the oldest MLB player to hit his first career home run. At 45 years old, he was the oldest active MLB player, and the last active MLB player who had played for the Montreal Expos. He also holds the record for most wins by a Latin-American born pitcher.

8. Joe Blanton and his wife own a three-acre vineyard on Howell Mountain that produces cabernet sauvignon in St. Helena, California.

9. Jim Fregosi was the last player to retire from the MLB who was a member of the "original" Los Angeles Angels.

10. On January 30, 2020, Peter Bourjos was hired as a scout for the Colorado Rockies.

CHAPTER 10:

OUTFIELDERS

QUIZ TIME!

1. Don Baylor played six seasons with the California Angels. Which of the teams below did he NOT play for during his 19-season career?

    a. Oakland Athletics
    b. Baltimore Orioles
    c. Chicago White Sox
    d. New York Yankees

2. Torii Hunter won nine Gold Glove Awards during his 19-season MLB career.

    a. True
    b. False

3. What year was Reggie Jackson inducted into the National Baseball Hall of Fame?

    a. 1991
    b. 1993

c. 1995

d. 1999

4. Mark Trumbo did NOT win a World Series championship in his 10-year MLB career.

   a. True

   b. False

5. How many MLB All-Star Games was Chone Figgins named to in his 12-year MLB career?

   a. 4

   b. 3

   c. 2

   d. 1

6. Tim Salmon was named the American League Rookie of the Year in which year?

   a. 1992

   b. 1993

   c. 1994

   d. 1995

7. Jim Edmonds played seven seasons with the Anaheim Angels.

   a. True

   b. False

8. During his 14-season MLB career, Darin Erstad played for the Los Angeles Angels, Houston Astros, and which team?

   a. San Francisco Giants

   b. San Diego Padres

c. Kansas City Royals

d. Chicago White Sox

9. What year was Dave Winfield inducted into the National Baseball Hall of Fame?

   a. 2000

   b. 2001

   c. 2002

   d. 2003

10. How many Gold Glove Awards did Fred Lynn win during his 17-year MLB career?

    a. 1

    b. 2

    c. 3

    d. 4

11. How many seasons did Kole Calhoun play for the Los Angeles Angels?

    a. 6

    b. 7

    c. 8

    d. 9

12. Bobby Abreu was named to only two MLB All-Star Games during his 18-season MLB career.

    a. True

    b. False

13. How many seasons did Peter Bourjos play for the Los Angeles Angels?

a. 6

b. 5

c. 4

d. 3

14. How many Silver Slugger Awards did former Angels outfielder Josh Hamilton win during his nine-season MLB career?

   a. 1

   b. 2

   c. 3

   d. 4

15. Over the course of his 10-year MLB career, Hideki Matsui played for the Los Angeles Angels, New York Yankees, Tampa Bay Rays, and which team?

   a. Seattle Mariners

   b. Oakland Athletics

   c. Toronto Blue Jays

   d. Atlanta Braves

16. What year was Rickey Henderson inducted into the National Baseball Hall of Fame?

   a. 2004

   b. 2007

   c. 2009

   d. 2011

17. How many seasons did Juan Rivera play for the Los Angeles Angels?

a. 3

b. 4

c. 5

d. 6

18. How many Gold Glove Awards did Vernon Wells win during his 15-year MLB career?

   a. 2

   b. 3

   c. 4

   d. 5

19. Over the course of his eight-season MLB career, Bo Jackson played for the California Angels, Chicago White Sox, and which tream?

   a. Los Angeles Dodgers

   b. San Diego Padres

   c. Kansas City Royals

   d. Florida Marlins

20. Former Angel Gary Matthews Jr. is the son of former MLB player Gary Matthews.

   a. True

   b. False

QUIZ ANSWERS

1. C – Chicago White Sox

2. A – True

3. B – 1993

4. A – True

5. D – 1

6. B – 1993

7. A – True

8. D – Chicago White Sox

9. B – 2001

10. D – 4

11. C – 8

12. A – True

13. B – 5

14. C – 3

15. B – Oakland Athletics

16. C – 2009

17. D – 6

18. B – 3

19. C – Kansas City Royals

20. A – True

DID YOU KNOW?

1. Mike Trout has played for the Los Angeles Angels since the 2011 season. He has been named a three-time American League MVP, 2012 American League Rookie of the Year, eight-time MLB All-Star, eight-time Silver Slugger Award winner, two-time All-Star MVP, 2019 Major League Player of the Year, and 2012 Wilson Overall Defensive Player of the Year.

2. Don Baylor spent six seasons of his 19-season MLB career with the California Angels. He also played for the Oakland Athletics, Baltimore Orioles, New York Yankees, Boston Red Sox, and Minnesota Twins. He was also the manager of the Colorado Rockies from 1993 to 1998 and the Chicago Cubs from 2000 to 2002. He was named the 1995 National League Manager of the Year. He is a World Series champion, one-time MLB All-Star and MVP, and three-time Silver Slugger Award winner.

3. Torii Hunter spent five seasons of his 19-season MLB career with the Los Angeles Angels. He also played for the Minnesota Twins and the Detroit Tigers. He is a five-time MLB All-Star, nine-time Gold Glove Award winner, and two-time Silver Slugger Award winner.

4. Jim Edmonds spent seven seasons of his 17-season MLB career with the California/Anaheim Angels. He also played for the St. Louis Cardinals, San Diego Padres, Chicago

Cubs, Cincinnati Reds, and Milwaukee Brewers. He is a four-time MLB All-Star, one-time Silver Slugger Award winner, eight-time Gold Glove Award winner, and one-time World Series champion.

5. Reggie Jackson spent five seasons of his 21-season MLB career with the California Angels. He also played for the Oakland Athletics, New York Yankees, and Baltimore Orioles. He is a member of the National Baseball Hall of Fame, MVP, fourteen-time MLB All-Star, five-time World Series champion, two-time Silver Slugger Award winner, two-time World Series MVP, and 1973 Major League Player of the Year.

6. Dave Winfield played two seasons with the California Angels. He famously played for the New York Yankees, as well as the San Diego Padres, Minnesota Twins, Cleveland Indians, and Toronto Blue Jays. He is a member of the National Baseball Hall of Fame, a twelve-time MLB All-Star, 1992 World Series champion, seven-time Gold Glove Award winner, and six-time Silver Slugger Award winner.

7. Darin Erstad spent 11 seasons of his 14-season MLB career with the Los Angeles Angels. He also played for the Houston Astros and Chicago White Sox. He is a two-time MLB All-Star, three-time Gold Glove Award winner, one-time Silver Slugger Award winner, and 2002 World Series champion.

8. Fred Lynn spent four seasons of his 17-season MLB career with the California Angels. He also played for the Boston

Red Sox, Baltimore Orioles, Detroit Tigers, and San Diego Padres. He is a 1975 American League MVP, 1975 American League Rookie of the Year, 1979 American League batting title winner, nine-time MLB All-Star, four-time Gold Glove Award winner, 1982 ALCS MVP, and 1983 All-Star MVP.

9. Tim Salmon spent his entire 14-season career with the California/Anaheim/Los Angeles Angels. He was named the 1993 American League Rookie of the Year, won one Silver Slugger Award, and is a 2002 World Series champion.

10. Rickey Henderson only spent one season (32 games) with the Anaheim Angels out of his 25 seasons spent in the MLB. He also played for the Oakland Athletics, New York Yankees, San Diego Padres, New York Mets, Boston Red Sox, Los Angeles Dodgers, Seattle Mariners, and Toronto Blue Jays. He is a member of the National Baseball Hall of Fame, 1990 American League MVP, 1989 ALCS MVP, ten-time MLB All-Star, two-time World Series champion, one-time Gold Glove Award winner, three-time Silver Slugger Award winner and holds all-time career records in stolen bases and runs scored.

CHAPTER 11:

INFIELDERS

QUIZ TIME!

1. What year was Rod Carew inducted into the National Baseball Hall of Fame?

    a. 1987
    b. 1989
    c. 1991
    d. 1993

2. Erick Aybar played for the Los Angeles Angels for 10 seasons.

    a. True
    b. False

3. During his 11-season MLB career, Maicer Izturis played for the Los Angeles Angels, Montreal Expos, and which team?

    a. Houston Astros
    b. Texas Rangers

   c. Florida Marlins

   d. Toronto Blue Jays

4. Howie Kendrick won a 2019 World Series championship with which team?

   a. Los Angeles Dodgers

   b. Philadelphia Phillies

   c. Washington Nationals

   d. Houston Astros

5. So far, Andrelton Simmons has played for the Los Angeles Angels and the _____ (as of the 2020 season).

   a. Los Angeles Dodgers

   b. Atlanta Braves

   c. Washington Nationals

   d. Cincinnati Reds

6. How many World Series championships did David Eckstein win during his 10-season MLB career?

   a. 0

   b. 1

   c. 2

   d. 3

7. Orlando Cabrera won two Gold Glove Awards during his 15-season MLB career.

   a. True

   b. False

8. How many seasons did Carney Lansford play for the California Angels?

a. 2

b. 3

c. 6

d. 10

9. How many MLB All-Star Games was Bert Campaneris named to during his 19-season MLB career?

a. 3

b. 4

c. 5

d. 6

10. How many seasons did Jim Fregosi play for the California Angels?

a. 7

b. 9

c. 11

d. 14

11. So far, Albert Pujols has played for the Los Angeles Angels and which team?

a. St. Louis Cardinals

b. New York Yankees

c. Tampa Bay Rays

d. Texas Rangers

12. Bobby Grich won four Gold Glove Awards during his 17-season MLB career.

a. True

b. False

13. Which Angels infielder was named the 2002 World Series MVP?

    a. Adam Kennedy
    b. David Eckstein
    c. Troy Glaus
    d. Scott Spiezio

14. How many MLB All-Star Games was Doug DeCinces named to during his 15-season MLB career?

    a. 0
    b. 1
    c. 2
    d. 3

15. How many Silver Slugger Awards has Anthony Rendon won so far (as of the end of the 2020 season)?

    a. 0
    b. 1
    c. 2
    d. 4

16. Adam Kennedy was named the 2002 ALCS MVP.

    a. True
    b. False

17. In his MLB career, Mike Napoli played for the Los Angeles Angels of Anaheim, Cleveland Indians, Texas Rangers, and which team?

    a. Colorado Rockies
    b. Tampa Bay Rays

c. Boston Red Sox

d. New York Yankees

18. How many Silver Slugger Awards did Kendrys Morales win during his 13-season MLB career?

    a. 1

    b. 2

    c. 3

    d. 4

19. How many Gold Glove Awards did J.T. Snow win during his 16-season MLB career?

    a. 2

    b. 4

    c. 6

    d. 8

20. The Los Angeles Angels was the only American League team that David Freese played for in his MLB career.

    a. True

    b. False

QUIZ ANSWERS

1. C – 1991

2. A – True

3. D – Toronto Blue Jays

4. C – Washington Nationals

5. B – Atlanta Braves

6. C – 2

7. A – True

8. B – 3

9. D – 6

10. C – 11

11. A – St. Louis Cardinals

12. A – True

13. C – Troy Glaus

14. B – 1

15. C – 2

16. A – True

17. C – Boston Red Sox

18. A – 1

19. C – 6

20. A – True

DID YOU KNOW?

1. Rod Carew spent seven seasons of his 19-season MLB career with the California Angels. He also played for the Minnesota Twins. He is a member of the National Baseball Hall of Fame, 1977 American League MVP, eighteen-time MLB All-Star, 1967 American League Rookie of the Year, seven-time batting title champion, and 1977 Major League Player of the Year.

2. David Eckstein spent four seasons of his 10-season MLB career with the Anaheim Angels. He also played for the St. Louis Cardinals, San Diego Padres, Toronto Blue Jays, and Arizona Diamondbacks. He is a two-time MLB All-Star, two-time World Series champion, and 2006 World Series MVP.

3. Orlando Cabrera spent three seasons of his 15-season MLB career with the Los Angeles Angels. He also played for the Montreal Expos, Minnesota Twins, San Francisco Giants, Oakland A's, Boston Red Sox, Cincinnati Reds, Cleveland Indians, and Chicago White Sox. He is a one-time World Series champion and two-time Gold Glove Award winner.

4. Carney Lansford spent three seasons of his 15-season MLB career with the California Angels. He also played for the Oakland Athletics and Boston Red Sox. He is a one-time MLB All-Star, World Series champion, Silver Slugger Award winner, and batting title champion.

5. Bert Campaneris spent three seasons of his 19-season MLB career with the California Angels. He also played for the Oakland Athletics, Texas Rangers, and New York Yankees. He is a six-time MLB All-Star and three-time World Series champion.

6. Jim Fregosi spent 11 seasons of his 18-season MLB career with the California Angels. He also played for the Texas Rangers, New York Mets, and Pittsburgh Pirates. He was a six-time MLB All-Star and one-time Gold Glove Award winner. He was manager of the Angels from 1978 to 1981. He also managed the Chicago White Sox, Philadelphia Phillies, and Toronto Blue Jays.

7. Albert Pujols has been with the Los Angeles Angels since 2012. He played for the St. Louis Cardinals from 2001 to 2011. So far, he is a three-time MVP, ten-time MLB All-Star, 2001 National League Rookie of the Year, two-time World Series champion, two-time Gold Glove Award winner, six-time Silver Slugger Award winner, 2003 batting title champion, 2004 NLCS MVP, and three-time Major League Player of the Year.

8. Bobby Grich spent 10 seasons of his 17-season MLB career with the California Angels. He also played for the Baltimore Orioles. He is a six-time MLB All-Star, four-time Gold Glove Award winner, and one-time Silver Slugger Award winner.

9. Adam Kennedy spent seven seasons of his 14-season MLB career with the Anaheim/Los Angeles Angels. He also

played for the St. Louis Cardinals, Los Angeles Dodgers, Washington Nationals, Seattle Mariners, and Oakland A's. He is a 2002 World Series champion and 2002 ALCS MVP.

10. Howie Kendrick spent nine seasons of his MLB career with the Los Angeles Angels. So far, he has also played for the Washington Nationals, Los Angeles Dodgers, and Philadelphia Phillies. He is a one-time MLB All-Star, 2019 World Series champion, and 2019 NLCS MVP.

CHAPTER 12:

PITCHERS & CATCHERS

QUIZ TIME!

1. Former Angels manager Mike Scioscia played his entire MLB career as a catcher for which team?

    a. New York Yankees

    b. Los Angeles Dodgers

    c. Oakland A's

    d. Kansas City Royals

2. Jered Weaver spent his entire 12-season MLB career with the Los Angeles Angels.

    a. True

    b. False

3. Which team did former Angels pitcher John Lackey NOT play for during his 15-season MLB career?

    a. Boston Red Sox

    b. Chicago Cubs

    c. Texas Rangers

    d. St. Louis Cardinals

4. What year did Frank Tanana win the American League pitching title?

    a. 1974
    b. 1975
    c. 1976
    d. 1977

5. What year did Bartolo Colon win a Cy Young Award as a member of the Angels?

    a. 2004
    b. 2005
    c. 2006
    d. 2007

6. During his 12-season MLB career, Mike Witt played for the California Angels and which team?

    a. Atlanta Braves
    b. Oakland A's
    c. New York Yankees
    d. New York Mets

7. Former Angels catcher Bengie Molina is the brother of Cardinals star catcher Yadier Molina.

    a. True
    b. False

8. How many MLB All-Star Games was Ervin Santana named to during his 15-season MLB career?

    a. 0
    b. 1

c. 2

d. 5

9. How many different MLB teams did Bartolo Colon play for during his 21-year MLB career?

   a. 7

   b. 9

   c. 11

   d. 15

10. How many MLB All-Star Games was Dan Haren named to during his 13-season MLB career?

   a. 0

   b. 2

   c. 3

   d. 5

11. During his 17-year MLB career, pitcher Chuck Finley played for the Angels, St. Louis Cardinals, and which team?

   a. Colorado Rockies

   b. Pittsburgh Pirates

   c. Cleveland Indians

   d. Oakland A's

12. Jeff Mathis spent the first seven seasons of his MLB career with the Los Angeles Angels.

   a. True

   b. False

13. How many wins did Nolan Ryan record during his 1974 season with the California Angels?

    a. 20
    b. 22
    c. 23
    d. 25

14. How many Gold Glove Awards did Mark Langston win during his 16-season MLB career?

    a. 3
    b. 5
    c. 7
    d. 9

15. Jarrod Washburn pitched for three teams during his 12-year MLB career, the Angels, Detroit Tigers, and which team?

    a. New York Mets
    b. Arizona Diamondbacks
    c. Seattle Mariners
    d. San Diego Padres

16. Brian Downing played for the California Angels for 13 seasons.

    a. True
    b. False

17. How many Gold Glove Awards did Bob Boone win during his 19-season MLB career?

    a. 3
    b. 4

c. 5

d. 7

18. How many MLB All-Star Games was Francisco Rodriguez named to during his 16-year MLB career?

    a. 2

    b. 4

    c. 6

    d. 7

19. During his seven-season MLB career, Tyler Skaggs played for the Los Angeles Angels and which team?

    a. San Diego Padres

    b. Arizona Diamondbacks

    c. Colorado Rockies

    d. Oakland A's

20. Don Sutton was inducted into the National Baseball Hall of Fame in 1998.

    a. True

    b. False

QUIZ ANSWERS

1. B – Los Angeles Dodgers

2. B – False (He spent one season with the San Diego Padres.)

3. C – Texas Rangers

4. D – 1977

5. B – 2005

6. C – New York Yankees

7. A – True

8. C – 2

9. C – 11

10. C – 3

11. C – Cleveland Indians

12. A – True

13. B – 22

14. C – 7

15. C – Seattle Mariners

16. A – True

17. D – 7

18. C – 6

19. B – Arizona Diamondbacks

20. A – True

DID YOU KNOW?

1. Mike Witt spent 10 seasons of his 13-season MLB career with the California Angels. He also played for the New York Yankees. He is a two-time MLB All-Star.

2. Frank Tanana spent eight seasons of his 21-season MLB career with the California Angels. He also played for the Detroit Tigers, Texas Rangers, New York Mets, New York Yankees, and Boston Red Sox. He is a three-time MLB All-Star and 1977 American League ERA Title winner.

3. John Lackey spent eight seasons of his 15-season MLB career with the Los Angeles Angels. He also played for the Boston Red Sox, Chicago Cubs, and St. Louis Cardinals. He is a one-time MLB All-Star, three-time World Series champion, and 2007 American League ERA Title winner.

4. Chuck Finley spent 14 seasons of his 17-season MLB career with the California/Anaheim Angels. He also played for the Cleveland Indians and St. Louis Cardinals. He is a five-time MLB All-Star.

5. Nolan Ryan spent eight seasons of his 27-season MLB career with the California Angels. He also played for the Texas Rangers, Houston Astros, and New York Mets. He is a member of the National Baseball Hall of Fame, eight-time MLB All-Star, two-time ERA Title winner, and 1969 World Series champion.

6. Mark Langston spent eight seasons of his 16-season MLB career with the California/Anaheim Angels. He also played for the Seattle Mariners, San Diego Padres, Cleveland Indians, and Montreal Expos. He is a four-time MLB All-Star and seven-time Gold Glove Award winner.

7. Brian Downing spent 13 seasons of his 20-season MLB career with the California Angels. He also played for the Chicago White Sox and Texas Rangers. He is a two-time MLB All-Star.

8. Bob Boone spent seven seasons of his 19-season MLB career with the California Angels. He also played for the Philadelphia Phillies and Kansas City Royals. He is a four-time MLB All-Star, seven-time Gold Glove Award winner, and 1980 World Series champion.

9. Don Sutton spent three seasons of his 23-season MLB career with the California Angels. He also played for the Los Angeles Dodgers, Milwaukee Brewers, Houston Astros, and Oakland A's. He is a member of the National Baseball Hall of Fame, four-time MLB All-Star, 1980 ERA Title winner, and 1977 All-Star MVP.

10. There have been 10 no-hitters and one perfect game in Los Angeles Angels franchise history. Angels pitchers who have thrown no-hitters/perfect games include: Bo Belinsky, Clyde Wright, Nolan Ryan (three times), Mike Witt (twice), Mark Langston, Ervin Santana, Jered Weaver, Taylor Cole, and Felix Peña.

CHAPTER 13:

WORLD SERIES

QUIZ TIME!

1. How many World Series have the Los Angeles Angels won in franchise history?

    a. 0
    b. 1
    c. 2
    d. 3

2. How many AL pennants have the Los Angeles Angels won?

    a. 1
    b. 2
    c. 3
    d. 4

3. Which team did the Anaheim Angels face in the 2002 World Series?

    a. Atlanta Braves
    b. Arizona Diamondbacks

c. St. Louis Cardinals

d. San Francisco Giants

4. Which team did the Anaheim Angels face in the 2002 ALCS?

a. Boston Red Sox

b. New York Yankees

c. Minnesota Twins

d. Oakland A's

5. How many games did the 2002 World Series go?

a. 4

b. 5

c. 6

d. 7

6. Who was the manager of the Anaheim Angels during the 2002 World Series?

a. Terry Collins

b. Mike Scioscia

c. Joe Maddon

d. Doug Rader

7. The 2002 World Series took place from October 19 to October 27.

a. True

b. False

8. Who was the manager of the San Francisco Giants during the 2002 World Series?

a. Frank Robinson

b. Felipe Alou

c. Bruce Bochy

d. Dusty Baker

9. What was the final score when the San Francisco Giants won Game 1 of the 2002 World Series?

    a. 5-3

    b. 4-3

    c. 1-0

    d. 5-2

10. What was the final score when the Anaheim Angels won Game 2 of the 2002 World Series?

    a. 4-3

    b. 12-10

    c. 11-10

    d. 1-0

11. What was the final score when the Anaheim Angels won Game 3 of the 2002 World Series?

    a. 10-4

    b. 5-4

    c. 11-5

    d. 12-4

12. The San Francisco Giants won Game 4 of the 2002 World Series by a score of 4-3.

    a. True

    b. False

13. What was the final score when the San Francisco Giants won Game 5 of the 2002 World Series?

   a. 2-1
   b. 4-2
   c. 16-4
   d. 6-4

14. What was the final score when the Anaheim Angels won Game 6 of the 2002 World Series?

   a. 9-3
   b. 5-3
   c. 16-5
   d. 6-5

15. What was the final score when the Anaheim Angels won Game 7 of the 2002 World Series?

   a. 3-1
   b. 4-1
   c. 5-1
   d. 6-1

16. The Angels won Game 7, and thus the World Series, at Pacific Bell Park in San Francisco.

   a. True
   b. False

17. Who was the winning pitcher in Game 7 of the 2002 World Series?

   a. John Lackey
   b. Jarrod Washburn

c. Ramon Ortiz

d. Kevin Appier

18. How many total home runs did Troy Glaus hit during the 2002 World Series?

    a. 1

    b. 2

    c. 3

    d. 4

19. How many home runs did Tim Salmon hit in Game 2 of the 2002 World Series?

    a. 0

    b. 1

    c. 2

    d. 3

20. Game 7 of the 2002 World Series was Dusty Baker's final game as manager of the San Francisco Giants.

    a. True

    b. False

QUIZ ANSWERS

1. B – 1 (2002)

2. A – 1

3. D – San Francisco Giants

4. C – Minnesota Twins

5. D – 7

6. B – Mike Scioscia

7. A – True

8. D – Dusty Baker

9. B – 4-3

10. C – 11-10

11. A – 10-4

12. A – True

13. C – 16-4

14. D – 6-5

15. B – 4-1

16. B – False (They won at Angel Stadium.)

17. A – John Lackey

18. C – 3

19. C – 2

20. A – True

DID YOU KNOW?

1. During the 2002 World Series, Dusty Baker's son (then a toddler) was a Giants bat boy. Kenny Lofton hit a triple, and J.T. Snow rounded third on his way home. Dusty's son Darren then runs to home to collect Lofton's bat. Somehow, Snow reacted quickly enough and was able to grab Darren by the jacket to save him from being trampled by Giants... literally. It is one of the most famous, odd moments in World Series history. Darren is now a college baseball player at Cal Berkeley.

2. In 2002, the Anaheim Angels became the first American League team not from the AL East Division to win the World Series since the Minnesota Twins in 1991.

3. In 2002, the Anaheim Angels became the first American League Wild Card winner to win the World Series. Currently, 2002 is still the only time the Angels have won a Wild Card berth.

4. By capturing their 2002 World Series title, the Angels therefore broke the supposed "curse" upon them, stemming from the fact that Angel Stadium was built on an ancient Native American burial ground.

5. The 2002 championship game was the last time a franchise would win its first World Series title until 2017 when the Houston Astros won their first. Teams that still have not won a World Series championship (as of the end of the

2020 season) include the Tampa Bay Rays, Colorado Rockies, Seattle Mariners, Milwaukee Brewers, San Diego Padres, and Texas Rangers.

6. The Angels won the 2002 World Series despite scoring fewer runs (41) than the Giants (44).

7. Angels pitcher John Lackey became the first rookie pitcher to win a World Series Game 7 since 1909.

8. Fox's telecast of the 2002 World Series marked the first time the World Series was telecast in high definition.

9. The 2002 World Series was the first World Series since the 1995 inception of the Wild Card in the MLB (and the last until 2014) in which both wild card teams faced each other for the title.

10. "Here's the pitch to Lofton. Fly ball, center field, Erstad says he's got it, Erstad MAKES THE CATCH! THE ANAHEIM ANGELS ARE THE CHAMPIONS OF BASEBALL!" — Rory Markas calling the final out of Game 7 of the 2002 World Series. The 2002 championship game was the only World Series called by Angels play-by-play commentator, Rory Markas, who passed away after a heart attack in January 2010.

CHAPTER 14:

HEATED RIVALRIES

QUIZ TIME!

1. Which team does NOT play in the American League West with the Los Angeles Angels?

   a. Oakland A's

   b. Los Angeles Dodgers

   c. Seattle Mariners

   d. Houston Astros

2. The Kansas City Royals were a part of the American League West Division from 1969 to 1993.

   a. True

   b. False

3. Which current AL West team moved to the division in 2013?

   a. Texas Rangers

   b. Houston Astros

   c. Oakland A's

   d. Seattle Mariners

4. What current American League West team has the most AL West championships?

    a. Houston Astros

    b. Seattle Mariners

    c. Oakland A's

    d. Texas Rangers

5. What is a series with fellow Los Angeles rival, the Dodgers, called?

    a. California Series

    b. Hollywood Series

    c. Freeway Series

    d. Highway Series

6. What year did the Angels and Dodgers have their first meeting?

    a. 1968

    b. 1970

    c. 1997

    d. 2000

7. The Angels have the most wins in the Freeway Series.

    a. True

    b. False

8. The Angels have one World Series championship. How many do the Oakland A's have?

    a. 4

    b. 7

    c. 8

    d. 9

9. The Angels have one World Series championship. How many do the Texas Rangers have?

    a. 0
    b. 1
    c. 2
    d. 3

10. The Angels have one World Series championship. How many do the Houston Astros have?

    a. 0
    b. 1
    c. 2
    d. 3

11. The Angels have one World Series championship. How many do the Seattle Mariners have?

    a. 0
    b. 1
    c. 2
    d. 3

12. The Los Angeles Angels and Los Angeles Dodgers have never met in the MLB postseason.

    a. True
    b. False

13. Which player has NOT played for both the Angels and the Oakland A's?

    a. Bert Campaneris
    b. Hideki Matsui

   c. Andrelton Simmons

   d. Reggie Jackson

14. Which player has NOT played for both the Angels and the Texas Rangers?

   a. Josh Hamilton

   b. Jim Fregosi

   c. Brian Downing

   d. Torii Hunter

15. Which player has NOT played for both the Angels and the Seattle Mariners?

   a. Chone Figgins

   b. Erick Aybar

   c. Mark Langston

   d. Kendrys Morales

16. As of the end of the 2020 season, the last time the Angels won the AL West Division was 2014.

   a. True

   b. False

17. Which player has NOT played for both the Angels and the Houston Astros?

   a. John Lackey

   b. Darin Erstad

   c. Hank Conger

   d. Don Sutton

18. Which player has NOT played for both the Angels and the Los Angeles Dodgers?

a. Dan Haren

b. Howie Kendrick

c. Brian Downing

d. Bobby Abreu

19. Which team was NOT a former member of the AL West?

a. Chicago White Sox

b. Chicago Cubs

c. Kansas City Royals

d. Minnesota Twins

20. The Houston Astros and Seattle Mariners are tied for the least AL West championships, with three each (as of the end of the 2020 season).

a. True

b. False

QUIZ ANSWERS

1. B – Los Angeles Dodgers

2. A – True

3. B – Houston Astros

4. C – Oakland A's

5. C – Freeway Series

6. C – 1997

7. A – True (70-60)

8. D – 9

9. A – 0

10. B – 1

11. A – 0

12. A – True

13. C – Andrelton Simmons

14. D – Torii Hunter

15. B – Erick Aybar

16. A – True

17. A – John Lackey

18. C – Brian Downing

19. B – Chicago Cubs

20. A – True

DID YOU KNOW?

1. The Oakland A's have the most American League West championships, with 17 (as of the end of the 2020 season). The Los Angeles Angels have nine, the Texas Rangers have seven, the Seattle Mariners and Houston Astros have three each. Former teams of the division who won AL West championships include: Kansas City Royals (6), Minnesota Twins (4), and Chicago White Sox (2). The most recent AL West Division champions are the Oakland A's (2020). The Angels have not won the AL West since 2014 (as of the end of the 2020 season).

2. The Angels and Texas Rangers have each pitched a perfect game against each other, making them the only pair of MLB teams to have done so. Mike Witt pitched a perfect game for the Angels against the Rangers in 1984 at Arlington Stadium, and Kenny Rogers pitched for the Rangers against the Angels in 1994.

3. In 2014, two MVPs were chosen from the same metropolitan area, with the Angels' outfielder Mike Trout winning the American League MVP and the Dodgers' pitcher Clayton Kershaw winning National League MVP for the year. This occurred again in 2019 when the Angels' Trout and the Dodgers' Cody Bellinger won their league's respective MVP awards

4. The Angels and Dodgers are 31.7 miles apart via I-5. Angel Stadium is further south than Dodger Stadium.

5. In 1995, the Seattle Mariners and California Angels were tied for the AL West division championship and played in a tie-breaker game. The Mariners won 9-1 to claim the division.

6. Bobby Abreu, Joe Blanton, Garret Anderson, Bill Buckner, Alberto Callaspo, Jesse Chavez, Chone Figgins, David Freese, Dan Haren, Rickey Henderson, Scott Kazmir, Howie Kendrick, Adam Kennedy, Mat Latos, Don Sutton, Shane Victorino, and Fernando Valenzuela have all played for both the Angels and the Los Angeles Dodgers.

7. Don Baylor, Mike Aldrete, Andrew Bailey, Franklin Barreto, Joe Blanton, Orlando Cabrera, Trevor Cahill, Alberto Callaspo, Bert Campaneris, Rickey Henderson, Bartolo Colon, Colin Cowgill, Brian Fuentes, Craig Gentry, Dan Haren, Reggie Jackson, Adam Kennedy, Carney Lansford, Hideki Matsui, Kendrys Morales, Dave Parker, Tony Phillips, Vic Power, Jesse Chavez, Huston Street, Don Sutton, and Scott Kazmir have all played for both the Angels and the Oakland A's.

8. Bobby Abreu, Bo Belinsky, Jason Castro, Hank Conger, Darin Erstad, Zack Greinke, LaTroy Hawkins, Scott Kazmir, Cameron Maybin, Bud Norris, Nolan Ryan, J.B. Shuck, Max Stassi, and Don Sutton have all played for both the Angels and the Houston Astros.

9. Sandy Alomar, Bobby Bonds, Bert Campaneris, Jesse Chavez, Bartolo Colon, Brian Downing, Jim Fregosi, Craig Gentry, Jason Grilli, Vladimir Guerrero, Josh Hamilton, Kevin Jepsen, Ian Kinsler, Jeff Mathis, Bengie Molina, Mike Napoli, Nolan Ryan, Frank Tanana, Mark Teixeira, Jerome Williams, Mitch Williams, and C.J. Wilson have all played for both the Angels and the Texas Rangers.

10. Danny Espinosa, Chone Figgins, Brian Fuentes, Rickey Henderson, Chris Iannetta, Raul Ibañez, Adam Kennedy, Casey Kotchman, Mark Langston, Cameron Maybin, Kendrys Morales, Harold Reynolds, Mark Trumbo, Bobby Valentine, Jason Vargas, Fernando Rodney, and Jarrod Washburn have all played for both the Angels and the Seattle Mariners.

CHAPTER 15:

THE AWARDS SECTION

QUIZ TIME!

1. Which California Angels player won the American League MVP Award in 1979?

    a. Carney Lansford
    b. Bert Campaneris
    c. Rod Carew
    d. Don Baylor

2. As of the end of the 2020 season, Mike Scioscia is the only Angels manager to ever win the American League Manager of the Year Award.

    a. True
    b. False

3. Which Los Angeles Angels pitcher won the Cy Young Award in 1964?

    a. Bo Belinsky
    b. Dean Chance

   c. Fred Newman

   d. None of the above

4. Which Los Angeles Angels player most recently won the American League Rookie of the Year Award (as of the end of the 2020 season)?

   a. Tim Salmon

   b. Kole Calhoun

   c. Mike Trout

   d. Shohei Ohtani

5. Which Los Angeles Angels player won the 2013 Wilson Overall Defensive Player of the Year Award?

   a. Mike Trout

   b. Josh Hamilton

   c. J.B. Shuck

   d. Kole Calhoun

6. Which Los Angeles Angels player won a Silver Slugger Award in 1995?

   a. J.T. Snow

   b. Chili Davis

   c. Tim Salmon

   d. Jim Edmonds

7. No Los Angeles Angels player has ever won the MLB Home Run Derby.

   a. True

   b. False

8. Which Angels player was named the DHL Hometown Hero? (Voted by MLB fans as the most outstanding player in franchise history.)

   a. Rod Carew

   b. Nolan Ryan

   c. Jim Fregosi

   d. Tim Salmon

9. Who was the first Los Angeles Angels player to win an American League Gold Glove Award?

   a. Jim Fregosi

   b. Vic Power

   c. Bobby Knoop

   d. Ken Berry

10. Who was the first Los Angeles Angels player to win a Silver Slugger Award?

    a. Bobby Grich

    b. Rick Burleson

    c. Reggie Jackson

    d. Both A and B

11. Which Los Angeles Angels pitcher won a Cy Young Award in 2005?

    a. John Lackey

    b. Ervin Santana

    c. Bartolo Colon

    d. Jarrod Washburn

12. In 2003, the 2002 Anaheim Angels were awarded the ESPY Award for "Outstanding Team."

    a. True
    b. False

13. Tim Salmon was named the American League Rookie of the Year in which year?

    a. 1989
    b. 1990
    c. 1993
    d. 1995

14. Mike Trout was named the MLB All-Star Game MVP in 2014 and which other year?

    a. 2015
    b. 2016
    c. 2017
    d. 2018

15. Which Los Angeles Angels player won the 2009 Branch Rickey Award for his exceptional community service?

    a. Howie Kendrick
    b. Torii Hunter
    c. Jered Weaver
    d. Mike Napoli

16. Mark Langston won five consecutive American League Gold Glove Awards from 1991 to 1995.

    a. True
    b. False

17. Which Los Angeles Angels player was named the 1962 MLB All-Star Game MVP?

    a. Tom Burgess

    b. Jim Fregosi

    c. Leon Wagner

    d. Dean Chance

18. Which California Angels player won a Silver Slugger Award in 1990?

    a. Dave Winfield

    b. Wally Joyner

    c. Chili Davis

    d. Lance Parrish

19. How many Gold Glove Awards did Jim Edmonds win during his time with the Anaheim Angels?

    a. 0

    b. 1

    c. 2

    d. 3

20. Mike Trout has NEVER won a Gold Glove Award.

    a. True

    b. False

QUIZ ANSWERS

1. D – Don Baylor

2. A – True (He won in 2002 and 2009.)

3. B – Dean Chance

4. D – Shohei Ohtani (2018)

5. C – J.B. Shuck

6. C – Tim Salmon

7. B – False (Three Angels won: Wally Joyner (1986), Garret Anderson (2003), Vladimir Guerrero (2007).)

8. A – Rod Carew

9. B – Vic Power (1964)

10. D – Both A and B

11. C – Bartolo Colon

12. A – True

13. C – 1993

14. A – 2015

15. B – Torii Hunter

16. A – True

17. C – Leon Wagner

18. D – Lance Parrish

19. C – 2

20. A – True

DID YOU KNOW?

1. The Los Angeles Angels have two different pitchers who have been named Cy Young Award winners in franchise history: Dean Chance (1964) and Bartolo Colon (2005).

2. The Los Angeles Angels have had 12 different players win Silver Slugger Awards in franchise history: Bobby Grich and Rick Burleson (1981), Reggie Jackson and Doug DeCinces (1982), Lance Parrish (1990), Tim Salmon (1995), Darin Erstad (2000), Troy Glaus (2000, 2001), Garret Anderson (2002), Vladimir Guerrero (2004, 2005, 2006, 2007), Torii Hunter (2009), and Mike Trout (2012, 2013, 2014, 2015, 2016, 2018, 2019).

3. The Los Angeles Angels have three different players who have been named American League Rookie of the Year in franchise history: Tim Salmon (1993), Mike Trout (2012), and Shohei Ohtani (2018).

4. The Los Angeles Angels have had 20 different players win Gold Glove Awards in franchise history: Ken Berry (1972), Bob Boone (1982, 1986, 1987, 1988), Orlando Cabrera (2007), Jim Edmonds (1997, 1998), Darin Erstad (2000, 2002, 2004), Jim Fregosi (1967), Bobby Knoop (1966, 1967, 1968), Mark Langston (1991, 1992, 1993, 1994, 1995), Rick Miller (1978), Bengie Molina (2002, 2003), Gary Pettis (1985, 1986), Vic Power (1964), J.T. Snow (1995, 1996), Jim Spencer (1970), Devon White (1988, 1989), Torii Hunter (2008, 2009), Erick

Aybar (2011), Kole Calhoun (2015), and Martin Maldonado and Andrelton Simmons (2017).

5. Three Los Angeles Angels players have ever been named MVP in franchise history: Don Baylor (1979), Vladimir Guerrero (2004), and Mike Trout (2014, 2016, 2019).

6. There has never been a Triple Crown winner in Los Angeles Angels franchise history.

7. Fred Lynn won the 1982 ALCS MVP Award. Adam Kennedy won the 2002 ALCS MVP Award.

8. Troy Glaus is the only Angels player to win the World Series MVP Award so far in franchise history (2002).

9. Mike Trout was named the Baseball America Major League Player of the Year in 2012, 2013, and 2016.

10. Tim Salmon was named the Baseball America Minor League Player of the Year in 1992, and Mike Trout was named the Baseball American Minor League Player of the Year in 2011.

CHAPTER 16:

THE HEART OF ORANGE COUNTY

QUIZ TIME!

1. Which famous theme park is located in Anaheim?

   a. SeaWorld

   b. Universal Studios

   c. Disney World

   d. Disneyland

2. The city of Anaheim was named after the nearby Santa Ana River and "heim," a German term for home, thereby creating the name "Ana-heim."

   a. True

   b. False

3. Which fast food franchise opened their first full service restaurant in Anaheim?

   a. McDonald's

   b. Burger King

   c. Carl's Jr.

   d. Wendy's

4. The creator of which cartoon series was born in Anaheim?

    a. *The Simpsons*

    b. *SpongeBob SquarePants*

    c. *South Park*

    d. *Scooby Doo*

5. Which singer went to high school in Anaheim?

    a. Beyoncé

    b. Katy Perry

    c. Gwen Stefani

    d. Ariana Grande

6. What is the name of Anaheim's NHL team?

    a. Anaheim Devils

    b. Anaheim Sharks

    c. Anaheim Kings

    d. Anaheim Ducks

7. The Anaheim Convention Center is the largest exhibit facility on the West Coast.

    a. True

    b. False

8. What is the name of the Anaheim Ducks' arena?

    a. United Center

    b. Bridgestone Arena

    c. Honda Center

    d. SAP Center

9. What type of berry originated in Anaheim?

    a. Blueberry
    b. Boysenberry
    c. Blackberry
    d. Raspberry

10. What year did Disneyland officially open to the public?

    a. 1935
    b. 1945
    c. 1955
    d. 1965

11. What is the name of the Disneyland Resort park that opened in 2001?

    a. Animal Kingdom
    b. Epcot
    c. Hollywood Studios
    d. California Adventure

12. Anaheim used to have an American Basketball Association (ABA) team called the Anaheim Amigos.

    a. True
    b. False

13. Which celebrity's first job was working at the Main Street Magic Shop at Disneyland?

    a. Tom Hanks
    b. Eddie Murphy
    c. Steve Martin
    d. Jack Black

14. What is the population of Anaheim (as of 2020)?

    a. 308,911

    b. 349,964

    c. 379,503

    d. 399,492

15. Which famous athlete attended high school in Anaheim?

    a. LeBron James

    b. Tom Brady

    c. Steph Curry

    d. Tiger Woods

16. Anaheim was founded by German immigrants from San Francisco in 1857.

    a. True

    b. False

17. How many years did it take to build Disneyland Park?

    a. 1

    b. 3

    c. 7

    d. 9

18. What is John Wayne International Airport-Orange County's code?

    a. JOC

    b. JWA

    c. SNA

    d. OCA

19. How many Stanley Cup championships have the Anaheim
    Ducks won (as of the end of the 2020 NHL season)?

    a. 0
    b. 1
    c. 2
    d. 3

20. Anaheim is the oldest city in Orange County, California.

    a. True
    b. False

QUIZ ANSWERS

1. D – Disneyland

2. A – True

3. C – Carl's Jr.

4. B – *SpongeBob SquarePants*

5. C – Gwen Stefani

6. D – Anaheim Ducks

7. A – True

8. C – Honda Center

9. B – Boysenberry

10. C – 1955

11. D – California Adventure

12. A – True

13. C – Steve Martin

14. B – 349,964

15. D – Tiger Woods

16. A – True

17. A – 1

18. C – SNA

19. B – 1

20. A – True

DID YOU KNOW?

1. Anaheim was founded by wine makers and grape farmers. After grape crops failed, oranges became the largest crop of the city. The Disneyland Resort is built on what once was orange groves.

2. Walt Disney's apartment is located right above the Fire Station on Main Street where he would often stay.

3. The drawbridge on Sleeping Beauty's Castle actually works. It has only been lowered twice: once when the park opened in 1955 and again when Fantasyland had a makeover in the 1980s.

4. The Anaheim Packing House, a 1919 citrus-packing facility, is now home to more than 20 independent vendors serving an eclectic mix of ethnic cuisine, gourmet dishes, and American comfort food.

5. Anaheim's annual Halloween parade is one of the largest Halloween parades in the United States.

6. The Los Angeles Clippers played select games in Anaheim at Honda Center from 1994 through 1999 before moving permanently to Staples Center in Downtown Los Angeles.

7. The Los Angeles Rams played in Anaheim at Angel Stadium from 1980 through 1994 before moving to St. Louis, Missouri.

8. Anaheim is a charter city, which means their governing system is defined by its own charter document rather than by general law.

9. Anaheim's sister cities include Mito, Japan, and Vitoria-Gasteiz, Spain.

10. "To all who come to this happy place, welcome! Disneyland is your land. Here, age relives fond memories of the past . . . and here youth may savor the challenge and promise of the future. Disneyland is dedicated to the ideals, the dreams and the hard facts that created America . . . with the hope that it will be a source of inspiration to all the world." – Walt Disney, July 17, 1955, Disneyland Opening Day speech

CHAPTER 17:

THE RYAN EXPRESS

QUIZ TIME!

1. What is Nolan Ryan's full name?

    a. Nolan Lyle Ryan Jr.

    b. Lyle Nolan Ryan Jr.

    c. Lynn Nolan Ryan Jr.

    d. Nolan Lynn Ryan Jr.

2. During his MLB career, Nolan Ryan played for the Texas Rangers, Houston Astros, New York Mets, and the California Angels.

    a. True

    b. False

3. Where was Nolan Ryan born?

    a. Houston, Texas

    b. Refugio, Texas

    c. Frisco, Texas

    d. Dallas, Texas

4. When was Nolan Ryan born?

    a. January 13, 1947
    b. January 13, 1950
    c. January 31, 1950
    d. January 31, 1947

5. Nolan Ryan threw seven no-hitters in his MLB career.

    a. True
    b. False

6. How many total MLB records does Nolan Ryan currently hold?

    a. 61
    b. 51
    c. 41
    d. 31

7. Where did Nolan Ryan go to high school?

    a. Alvin High School
    b. Clear Creek High School
    c. Westwood High School
    d. Carroll High School

8. When Nolan Ryan was called up to the New York Mets in 1966, he was the second youngest player in the MLB.

    a. True
    b. False

9. Nolan Ryan was inducted into the Angels Hall of Fame in what year?

a. 1985

b. 1992

c. 1997

d. 2002

10. What is the name of Nolan Ryan's 1992 autobiography?

    a. *Nolan Ryan's Pitcher's Bible*

    b. *Throwing Heat*

    c. *Miracle Man*

    d. *The Road to Cooperstown*

11. Nolan Ryan played in the MLB for how many presidential administrations?

    a. 3

    b. 5

    c. 7

    d. 9

12. Nolan Ryan is one of only three players in MLB history to have his uniform number retired by at least three teams.

    a. True

    b. False

13. What year was Nolan Ryan inducted into the National Baseball Hall of Fame?

    a. 1995

    b. 1989

    c. 1990

    d. 1999

14. Nolan Ryan NEVER threw a perfect game and NEVER won a Cy Young Award.

    a. True
    b. False

15. Nolan Ryan is one of only 29 players in MLB history to pitch in how many different decades.

    a. 3
    b. 4
    c. 5
    d. 6

16. Nolan Ryan was drafted by the which team?

    a. Texas Rangers
    b. Houston Astros
    c. California Angels
    d. New York Mets

17. There is a Nolan Ryan statue in front of Angel Stadium.

    a. True
    b. False

18. How many All-Star Games was Nolan Ryan named to during his career?

    a. 7
    b. 8
    c. 9
    d. 10

19. Nolan Ryan has a charity whose mission is "to provide resources for youth, education and community development." What is the name of Ryan's charity?

    a. The Ryan Express Foundation
    b. The Ryan Foundation
    c. The Nolan Ryan Foundation
    d. The Nolan Foundation

20. Nolan Ryan used to soak his fingers in pickle juice to avoid and treat blisters.

    a. True
    b. False

QUIZ ANSWERS

1. C – Lynn Nolan Ryan Jr.

2. A – True

3. B – Refugio, Texas

4. D – January 31, 1947

5. A – True

6. B – 51

7. A – Alvin High School

8. A – True

9. B – 1992

10. C – *Miracle Man*

11. C – 7: Lyndon B. Johnson, Richard Nixon, Gerald Ford, Jimmy Carter, Ronald Reagan, George H.W. Bush, and Bill Clinton

12. A – True

13. D – 1999

14. A – True

15. B – 4

16. D – New York Mets

17. B – False

18. B – 8

19. C – The Nolan Ryan Foundation

20. A – True

DID YOU KNOW?

1. Nolan Ryan married his high school sweetheart, Ruth.

2. In May 2000, Nolan Ryan introduced Nolan Ryan Tender Age Beef to Texas markets. The beef was raised and sold on Ryan's personal ranch.

3. From August 2010 to October 2013, Nolan Ryan was part owner of the Texas Rangers.

4. In May 2014, Nolan Ryan published a cookbook called *The Nolan Ryan Beef and Barbecue Cookbook: Recipes from a Texas Kitchen*, full of over 75 recipes.

5. In November 2016, Nolan Ryan, along with David Ortiz and Barry Larkin, created Dugout Ventures, an equity group that focuses on baseball products and companies.

6. In April 2000, Nolan Ryan suffered a heart attack and underwent emergency double bypass surgery.

7. Nolan Ryan had an infamous fight/brawl with Robin Ventura in 1993 at Arlington Stadium.

8. Nolan Ryan used to be a newspaper boy. He delivered copies of the *Houston Post* every morning for several years.

9. Nolan Ryan played in the MLB for 27 years.

10. The New York Mets have never retired Nolan Ryan's number. The Mets are the only team he played for who has not retired his number. The Angels, Astros, and Rangers have.

CHAPTER 18:

VLAD

QUIZ TIME!

1. Where was Vladimir Guerrero born?

    a. Montreal, Canada

    b. San Juan, Puerto Rico

    c. Santo Domingo, Dominican Republic

    d. Nizao, Dominican Republic

2. Vladimir Guerrero is a member of the Angels Hall of Fame.

    a. True

    b. False

3. How many seasons did Vladimir Guerrero play in the MLB?

    a. 12

    b. 14

    c. 16

    d. 18

4. What year was Vladimir Guerrero inducted into the National Baseball Hall of Fame?

    a. 2016
    b. 2018
    c. 2019
    d. 2020

5. How many MLB All-Star Games was Vladimir Guerrero named to during his MLB career?

    a. 3
    b. 6
    c. 9
    d. 10

6. How many Silver Slugger Awards did Vladimir Guerrero win during his MLB career?

    a. 2
    b. 4
    c. 6
    d. 8

7. Vladimir Guerrero NEVER won a World Series championship.

    a. True
    b. False

8. Vladimir Guerrero was named the American League MVP in which year?

    a. 2004
    b. 2006

c. 2007

d. 2009

9. Vladimir Guerrero made his MLB debut in 1996 as a member of which team?

   a. Anaheim Angels

   b. Texas Rangers

   c. Montreal Expos

   d. Baltimore Orioles

10. Vladimir Guerrero played his final MLB game in 2011 as a member of which team?

    a. Los Angeles Angels of Anaheim

    b. Baltimore Orioles

    c. Texas Rangers

    d. Toronto Blue Jays

11. What MLB team does Vladimir Guerrero's son, Vladimir Guerrero Jr., currently play for (as of the 2020 season)?

    a. Texas Rangers

    b. Washington Nationals

    c. Baltimore Orioles

    d. Toronto Blue Jays

12. On September 26, 2011, Vladimir Guerrero surpassed Julio Franco as the all-time MLB leader for hits by a Dominican player. Adrián Beltré claimed the record from Guerrero in 2014.

    a. True

    b. False

13. How many home runs did Vladimir Guerrero hit during his MLB career?

   a. 419
   b. 429
   c. 449
   d. 489

14. What is Vladimir Guerrero's career batting average?

   a. .298
   b. .318
   c. .338
   d. .378

15. How many hits did Vladimir Guerrero record during his MLB career?

   a. 2,290
   b. 2,390
   c. 2,490
   d. 2,590

16. Vladimir Guerrero's brother, Wilton Guerrero, played in the MLB from 1996 to 2004.

   a. True
   b. False

17. During his 16-year MLB career, Vladimir Guerrero played for the Los Angeles Angels, Montreal Expos, Baltimore Orioles, and which team?

   a. Florida Marlins
   b. Los Angeles Dodgers

c. Texas Rangers

d. Toronto Blue Jays

18. How many RBIs did Vladimir Guerrero record during his MLB career?

   a. 1,296

   b. 1,496

   c. 1,696

   d. 1,896

19. Vladimir Guerrero helped lead the Angels to how many American League West championships between 2004 and 2009?

   a. 2

   b. 3

   c. 4

   d. 5

20. Vladimir Guerrero was named the 1997 National League Rookie of the Year.

   a. True

   b. False

QUIZ ANSWERS

1. D – Nizao, Dominican Republic

2. A – True

3. C – 16

4. B – 2018

5. C – 9

6. D – 8

7. A – True

8. A – 2004

9. C – Montreal Expos

10. B – Baltimore Orioles

11. D – Toronto Blue Jays

12. A – True

13. C – 449

14. B – .318

15. D – 2,590

16. A – True

17. C – Texas Rangers

18. B – 1,496

19. D – 5

20. B – False (He came in 6th place.)

DID YOU KNOW?

1. Vladimir Guerrero was named the Los Angeles Angels Player of the Year four times during his time on the team (2004, 2005, 2006, 2007).

2. Vladimir Guerrero was named the Double-A Player of the Year in 1996.

3. Vladimir Guerrero is a back-to-back two-time member of the 30-30 club (2001 and 2002).

4. On March 31, 2014, Vladimir Guerrero signed a one-day contract with the Los Angeles Angels of Anaheim and officially retired from the MLB.

5. Vladimir Guerrero was the first member of the National Baseball Hall of Fame to be depicted with an Angels cap on his plaque.

6. Vladimir Guerrero was inducted into the National Baseball Hall of Fame in 2018 along with Chipper Jones, Jim Thome, and Trevor Hoffman.

7. Vladimir Guerrero was known for batting without wearing batting gloves, a rarity in the MLB.

8. Vladimir Guerrero batted over .300 from 1997 to 2008. He drove in over 100 runs every season between 1998 and 2007, except for 2003.

9. Vlad Jr. was born in Montreal while his father was playing for the Montreal Expos.

10. Vladimir Guerrero was named to the Dominican Republic's roster for the 2006 World Baseball Classic; although, he withdrew due to the death of three of his cousins in a car accident.

CONCLUSION

Learn anything new? Now you truly are the ultimate Angels fan! Not only did you learn about the Halos of the modern era, but you also expanded your knowledge back to the early days of the franchise.

You learned about the Angels' origins and their history. You learned about the history of their uniforms and jersey numbers. You identified some famous quotes and read some of the craziest nicknames of all time. You learned more about powerhouse hitter Vladimir Guerrero. You also learned about current star Mike Trout and legendary pitcher Nolan Ryan. You were amazed by Angels stats and recalled some of the most infamous Angels trades and draft picks of all time. You broke down your knowledge by outfielders, infielders, pitchers, and catchers. You looked back on the Angels' championship, playoff feats, and the awards that came before, after, and during them. You also learned about the Angels' fiercest rivalries both inside and outside their division.

Every team in the MLB has a storied history, but the Angels have one of the most memorable of all. They have won one World Series championship with the backing of their devoted fans. Being the ultimate Angels fan takes knowledge and a whole lot of patience, which you tested with this book. Whether you knew every answer or were stumped by several questions, you learned some of the most interesting history that the game of baseball has to offer.

The deep history of the Angels franchise represents what we all love about the game of baseball. The heart, the determination, the tough times, and the unexpected moments, plus the players that inspire us and encourage us to do our best, because even if you get knocked down, there is always another game and another day.

With players like Mike Trout, Albert Pujols, and Andrelton Simmons, the future for the Halos continues to look bright. They have a lot to prove, but there is no doubt that this franchise will continue to be one of the most competitive teams in Major League Baseball year after year.

It's a new decade, which means there is a clean slate, ready to continue writing the history of the Los Angeles Angels. The ultimate Angels fan cannot wait to see what's to come for their beloved Halos.

Made in the USA
Las Vegas, NV
29 March 2022

46510114R00089